JOHN RAY

ESSEX NATURALIST

Ioannes Rajus. A.M.
Societatis Regiæ Socius.

W. Hibbart

Bathon: Sculp.
1760

JOHN RAY
(1627-1705)
ESSEX NATURALIST

A summary of his life, work and scientific significance

by
Stuart A. Baldwin
F.G.S., F.L.S.

1986

Baldwin's Books
Fossil Hall, Boars Tye Road, Silver End, Witham, Essex, England, CM8 3QA
Telephone: Silver End, STD Code (0376) 83502

PREFACE

This small booklet has been written at the request of Braintree District Council, in support of the **John Ray Celebrations**, being held in honour of the 300th anniversary of the publication of Ray's great work *Historia Plantarum*, (1686). In writing and publishing it, three aims have been foremost:

1. To provide a concise, inexpensive account of John Ray and his achievements, in answer to the question: "I've heard of him, but what did he do?"
2. To stimulate an interest in John Ray himself, in the hope that others, like myself, will be drawn to that masterly biography of him by Charles Raven: *John Ray Naturalist*.
3. To stimulate and encourage an interest in natural history in general, and conservation in particular; and to hope that others, through his example, will follow in the footsteps of *"Our countryman, the excellent Mr Ray."* (Gilbert White).

ACKNOWLEDGEMENTS

I would like to thank: Mrs Valerie Carpenter of Braintree District Council, for bringing John Ray to our attention; Mrs N.H.Jeanty-Raven for permission to dedicate this to her late husband and for access to his library; Professor W.T.Stearn for starting me off in the right direction; Miss M.A.Arber for helpful suggestions; Dr Max Walters for encouragement, reading part of the script and suggesting improvements; Mr & Mrs K.R.Crawshaw for proof reading and many improvements; Miss Gina Douglas, Librarian of the Linnaean Society and her staff for considerable help and the illustration on page 56; the Ray Society for permission to reproduce the illustration on page 40; Mrs Judith Diment, Botany Librarian, British Museum (Natural History), for help; Cambridge University Press for permission to quote from Canon Raven's life of Ray; Mr H.K.Swann of Wheldon and Wesley Ltd., for permission to quote from Ray's *Flora of Cambridgeshire*; the Library of the Royal Botanic Gardens, Kew, for the illustrations on pages 10 and 16; the Castle Museum Nottingham for the illustration on page 14; Terence Illsley for the photograph on page 4; and finally my wife for encouragement and help.

Stuart A.Baldwin, March, 1986.

CONTENTS

CHAPTER 1

JOHN RAY (1627-1705)

EARLY LIFE.

In November 1627, in the small village of Black Notley in Essex, some two miles south of Braintree, the thirty three year old local blacksmith, Roger Ray, and his wife Elizabeth, were expecting their third child. Their first son Roger, was three, and his sister Elizabeth, a year younger. The third Ray[1] duly arrived on Thursday 27th, and was christened John at Black Notley church on 6th December.

His name was almost certainly derived from that of his grandfather John Ray, whose second marriage produced eight children. The eldest of these, Roger was born in 1594 and was to become the father of the famous John. As Raven[2] mentions; little is known for sure about Ray's early childhood, other than that his elder brother died quite young, and that he at one time had smallpox.

Ray's birthplace still exists in Bakers Lane, Black Notley and is clearly marked 'John Ray Cottage'. The smithy that was attached to the cottage, has long been out of use[3] as such, though the large bellows are still in existence and can be seen in the museum in the Town Hall Centre at Braintree. A discovery of an old anvil that came from Black Notley, has recently been reported in the local paper, and could well be the one used by Ray's father.

From the fascination that blacksmith's forges have for all children, and particularly for boys, it can be inferred that Ray spent many hours of his childhood watching[4], and later, probably even helping his father at his skilled craft. As Raven suggests (1942, pp.7-8), Ray, from watching his father, was to draw from it *'his enthusiasm for methods of manufacture...It was this desire to see how things are made and how they function that gave him his conviction of the importance of anatomy, his skill in dissection, his insistence that specific differences must be based upon structural characteristics, not upon colour or size or habit. His birthright on his father's side qualified him for a serious attempt to base taxonomy upon a study of comparative anatomy and physiology.'*

Ray's mother probably had an even greater influence in shaping his personality, character, and subsequent life. Of her, Derham wrote[5] in 1760:

'She was a very religious and good woman, and of great use in her neighbourhood, particularly to her neighbours that were lame or sick, among whom she did great good, especially in chirurgical matters. Her death was much lamented by all sorts of persons in her neighbourhood.'

As the local 'herb-woman' she would have been respected by both villagers and the medical profession. She undoubtedly stimulated his interest in religion. From accompanying her on her plant-collecting trips in the surrounding countryside, he obviously derived great pleasure, and his life-long primary interest in plants. It was this interest that was to have such far-reaching consequences.

Though he learnt a great deal about the medical uses of plants from his mother, the great appeal for him was their intrinsic beauty, and most significantly, the plants themselves. This is particularly evident in the preface to his Catalogue of Cambridge Plants, in which he expresses his great delight in botanising. (See chapter 3).

BRAINTREE CHURCH,
ESSEX.

Engraved by E Roberts from a Sketch by W Deeble for the Excursions Through Essex.

St. Michael's Church, Braintree, as it appeared in 1819.
The Grammar School where Ray attended in in the south chapel.
From *Excursions Through Essex*, 1818-19.

In the seventeenth century, much plant lore was still inextricably linked with superstition, alchemy, legend, magic, and astrology, in a chaos of confusion. Thanks to his parents, Ray had a background that shaped and influenced his mind at an early age. This enabled him, as an adult, to bring order out of this chaos. There were other forces at work though that shared in this mind-shaping process, and for the first of these we must look to his school days.

BRAINTREE GRAMMAR SCHOOL.

The smithy was only a few hundred yards away from the church, and it is quite likely that either Thomas Goad, rector there till 1638, or his successor, Joseph Plume, had some influence in sending Ray to the Grammar School attached to St. Michael's Church in Braintree.

The school had then been in existence for about a hundred years, having been formed in the south chapel of the church. To this day, marks made by the sharpening of slate pencils, are still visible on the chancel pillar[6].

Ray attended the school for six and a half years from the age of ten. During this time he came under the master, a Mr Love. Little seems to be known of him, and Ray, in later life, when he had the opportunity of comparing his education with that of others, had a poor view of his schooling. Nevertheless, he received an excellent grounding in Latin, as is evidenced from his later skills. (He became one of the most fluent Latin writers of his age, and was as much at home in writing Latin as English).

He was certainly taught to write well, as his handwriting was not only of a very high standard, but was completely legible to the end of his life. Much of the teaching there, must also have trained his memory, ordered his mind, and given him a love of book-learning, as these became important features of his long and prolific scientific career.

There can be no doubt that, not only was he an exceptional pupil academically, but that his genius for friendship was already beginning to blossom. At the age of sixteen and a half, he obtained a scholarship to Cambridge University, largely thanks to the Vicar of Braintree, Samuel Collins. As a Cambridge graduate himself, Collins would have liked Ray to have gone to his old college - Trinity. However, under the terms of the will of a certain Thomas Hobbs, he was empowered to pay for two or three poor scholars to go to Cambridge, with preference being given to Catharine Hall. (Later to become St. Catharine's College). Ray became a beneficiary under the terms of this will and entered Catharine Hall in June 1644.

CAMBRIDGE UNIVERSITY.

At Cambridge, Ray's tutor was another Essex man, Daniel Duckfield. He was there for less than two years and then transferred to Trinity College. There are probably at least five reasons for this move: Duckfield died in 1645, Ray was not happy with the predominance of 'disputations[7]' as a teaching method at Catharine Hall, at Trinity[8] 'the politer Arts and Sciences were principally minded and cultivated.' and were much closer to Ray's interests, his brilliance had already become evident, and Collins's preference was already clear. He entered Trinity College on 21st November 1646 as a subsizar[9], and was placed under James Duport, Regius Professor of Greek.

4

Twentieth century pargetting on 'John Ray Cottage'
at Black Notley – Ray's birthplace.
Photograph by Terence Illsley.

One of Ray's fellow students under Duport was Isaac Barrow.
(He later become Professor of Mathematics at Cambridge and had
as his pupil and successor Isaac Newton). Of these, Duport said
later '"*The chief of all his pupils were Mr Ray and Dr Barrow"*,
to whom he esteemed none of the rest comparable.[10]'
Ray acquired great skill in Latin, Greek and Hebrew, and he
showed early promise as an orator and naturalist. He graduated
B.A. in 1647/8 and he and Barrow were both made Minor Fellows of
Trinity in 1649. Two years later he became a Major Fellow and a
succession of appointments then followed: Greek Lecturer (1651),
Mathematics Lecturer (1653), and Reader in Humanities in 1655.
His personal charm, amiable disposition, and ability to get
on with others are evidenced by his progress in the offices of
his college, in which he became Praelector, then Junior Dean and
twice College-Steward. He became eminent as a tutor and as a
preacher. One of Ray's contemporaries, Dr Tennison, who
subsequently became The Archbishop of Canterbury, is reported by
Derham[11] to have told him '*That Mr Ray was much celebrated in
his time in Cambridge, for his preaching solid and useful
divinity, instead of that enthusiastic stuff, which the sermons
of the time were generally filled with.*' Tennison was just one
of many friends Ray made during his time at Cambridge, who were
later to become distinguished.
Ray had many pupils, and several became close friends. Of
these, Francis Willughby was perhaps the closest, and he
certainly had a considerable influence in Ray's subsequent life.
Willughby, who was several years younger than Ray, was the only
son of Sir Francis Willughby of Middleton Hall in Warwickshire
and Lady Cassandra, the daughter of the first Earl of
Londonderry. He and Ray, struck up a remarkable relationship.
Willughby did well at Cambridge, and it was his idea of
producing a complete account of all living things, that fired
Ray's enthusiasm and provided the stimulus for him.
Willughby's cousin, Peter Courthope, of Danny in Sussex, was
another of Ray's pupils who became a close friend, and also
Phillip Skippon, the only son of Cromwell's Major-general of the
same name. Ray's other great friend at Cambridge was John Nidd
who had graduated there in the year Ray arrived, and who also
became a senior fellow of Trinity.
It was while he was at Cambridge in 1656, that his father
died, and Ray built Dewlands at Black Notley for his widowed
mother.
Chance can often play an important part in people's lives,
and in Ray's case it was an illness that struck him in 1650 that
was to have such far-reaching effects. It is possible that he
had been overworking, because, not only did he have a chest
complaint, but he was also affected mentally. It was during
recovery from this illness, that he found he had time on his
hands, and he started exploring the surrounding countryside. His
interest in plants was re-awakened, and not finding anyone to
help him in the University, he decided to study them himself.
Over the next six years he made many collecting trips in the
field, often in the company of one or more of his friends,
particularly Willughby, Nidd and Courthope. He made copious
notes, and then spent a further three years revising and putting
them into book form. In 1660 a small volume was published with
the title *Catalogus Plantarum circa Cantibrigiam nascentium*,
(Catalogue of Cambridge Plants). This was a work of such
scientific significance and importance that its effects are

6

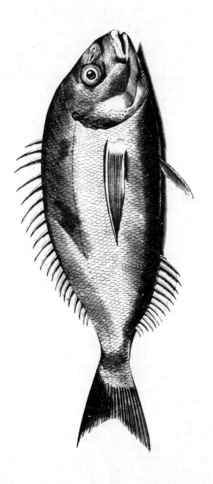

Aurata Sabriani.

Tab. V. 5.   Sumptibus D. Sam Pepys. Præs S.R.

One of the 187 plates from Willughby's *Historia Piscium*.
This was one of 79 plates paid for by Samuel Pepys,
the president of the Royal Society. (See p.51).

still with us today. Its effect on Ray however was even greater, as it was only the beginning of his scientific career. (The full story of the Cambridge Catalogue is given in chapter 3).

The achievement of Ray's Catalogue, was summed up by the Rev. W.L.P. Garnons, of Ulting in Essex, in his manuscript[12] life of Ray:

'When we consider the low condition of botanical science at that period, and the meagre construction of all previous catalogues, we cannot but express our surprise and admiration at this extraordinary production...This little volume, was received by the lovers of botany in the most favourable manner; and there can be no doubt but that it tended greatly to promote the study of plants, and to excite that interest for the science, which enabled him, in the later period of his life, to receive from those, who had, under his guidance, entered upon the same pursuit, that assistance, without which, it would have been scarcely possible for him to accumulate the mass of information which his numerous works everywhere contain.'

JOURNEYS IN BRITAIN AND ON THE CONTINENT

Even before the Catalogue was published, Ray had decided to extend and perfect his botanical studies. In August and September of 1685, he spent six weeks on his own, travelling through much of the Midlands and North Wales, with the express purpose of collecting and looking at more plants. The reception given to the Cambridge Catalogue was so encouraging, that he decided to produce a similar one for the whole of England. To do this he enlisted the help of his many friends, in sending him details. In addition, over the next ten years, with the exception of three years abroad, he made extensive tours over most of England and Wales, the Isle of Man, and part of Scotland. This was to obtain first-hand information, and was usually in the company of Willughby or Skippon, or sometimes both. The intention was, for Willughby to concentrate on zoology and Ray on plants, as part of their overall plan formulated earlier.

Ray however, was not just observing and collection botanical specimens. He had an extraordinary wide range of interests, and apart from helping Willughby with the zoology, he looked at fossils, geological phenomena, mining and industrial processes. He made collections of Proverbs, unusual English words and details of dialects, and all of these resulted in several pioneering books later.

At Cambridge, Ray occupied a position without any formal religious status, even though this was a requirement. He was persuaded to take up holy orders in 1660 and was ordained in December. Two years later, the Act of Uniformity was passed by Parliament. Under this, all Fellows of the University were required to declare, that those who taken an oath under the *Solemn League and Covenant*, were not obliged to keep to that oath. Though Ray himself had not taken this oath, he was a man of principle, and would not denigrate himself to say that an oath was not binding. As a result he had to give up his fellowship, and his livelihood, and leave Cambridge. This must have been a shattering blow to him, as he was obviously enjoying his academic life, and the use of libraries. Great as were Ray's achievements over the rest of his life, it is interesting to speculate what they might have been, with the full backing and resources of a great university behind him.

8

Engraved by T. Higham, from a Drawing by J. Greig for the Excursions through Essex.

FAULKBOURN HALL,
The Seat of J.J.C.Bullock. Esq.ʳ
ESSEX.

Pub.ᵈ ... ... by Longman & ... Patern ... ...

Faulkbourne Hall near Witham in Essex as it appeared
in 1818. It was Ray's home from 1677 - 1679.
From *Excursions Through Essex* 1818-19.

After settling his affairs at Cambridge, Ray spent six months as a tutor in the house of Thomas Bacon, of Friston Hall near Saxmundham in Suffolk. Before this however, Willughby had suggested a tour of the Continent to extend their biological studies. On April 18th, Willughby, Ray, Skippon and Nathaniel Bacon, a contemporary of Ray's at Trinity, set sail from Dover for Calais. The tour was to last for three years, and was probably regarded by Ray as one of the highlights of his life.

For Ray and Willughby, the primary purpose of the tour was to extend their knowledge of plants and animals respectively, though Ray also carried out much work on zoology. They worked, by collecting in the countryside wherever they went, starting in northern France and continuing through Belgium, Holland, the Rhineland, Switzerland, Austria and Italy. In Naples, the party split and Ray and Skippon went on to Malta and Sicily, returning via Rome, and Switzerland to Montpellier in the south of France. There, Ray met Dr Martin Lister, an Englishman who was to become a close friend, and Nicolaus Steno, the famous Danish anatomist and geologist. They also, whenever they had the opportunity, studied birds and fishes in markets and ports, and Ray built up a very fine collection of fishes from the Mediterranean.

Travel could not have been very comfortable in those days and various modes of transport are mentioned. They were pulled along the Rhine in a boat by man-power; at Schadwien their coach was drawn to the top of a hill by ten oxen, in Italy they sailed some of the way, and when, in 1666, the King of France ordered all Englishmen to leave, Ray used a fish-cart[13] to get to Calais.

Ray and Skippon recorded an incredible amount of detail of their observations, and both subsequently published books of the tour. In Ray's case, he had produced a Catalogue of Foreign Plants and his 'Observations' were included to add popular interest[14].

The tour was much more than just a collecting trip. For Ray it provided an important opportunity to meet other scientists, visit universities and museums, and study their libraries and collections. It broadened his outlook and provided him with enough scientific data, to occupy him for much of his remaining years. As Crowther[15] so aptly puts it: 'This tour was to him what the voyage of the Beagle was to Darwin.'

On his return to England, Ray spent the summer with various friends in Essex and Sussex, and caught up with the three-year backlog of reading that had accumulated. This included Hooke's Micrographia, and Boyle's Usefulness of Natural Philosophy. The winter was spent with Willughby, working on the collections from their tour, and in producing the Tables for Wilkins's Essay. (p.27). The next few years were spent based with Willughby, either at Middleton or Wollaton, though much of this time was spent in travelling, gathering data for the Catalogue of English Plants. In 1667, after several requests to Ray, he accepted an invitation from the Royal Society and was admitted a Fellow. One of his earliest communications to the Society was a report on some experiments he and Willughby had carried out on the movement of sap in trees. (p.33).

In 1670, his second major work in botany was complete and the Catalogue of English Plants was published. (p.29). In the same year he also published A Collection of English Proverbs. (p.67). Two years later in July 1672, disaster struck, and his great friend and benefactor, Willughby, died at the age of 37.

10

Ray's home Dewlands at Black Notley where he wrote much of his work.

It was destroyed by fire in 1900.

The original engraving was presented to the Ray Society by Mr J.H. Pattison a Witham solicitor and the then owner, in 1848 and is now in the Library of the Royal Botanical Gardens, Kew.

THE YEARS OF PRODIGIOUS OUTPUT

'The output of those years is probably the largest in sheer mass of material, that any one man has produced since Aristotle.[16]

Ray had been appointed an executor of Willughby's will, and under the terms of this, he was given an annuity of £60, and the responsibility for educating the two young sons. Though the annuity was not a large amount, it was sufficient to enable Ray to spend the rest of his life working at natural history.

He stayed on at Middleton and in 1673 published the Catalogue of European Plants combined with his Observations. Later that year he married Margaret Oakley, a member of the household at Middleton. She was only nineteen, but despite the disparity in their ages, all the subsequent evidence suggests that they had a very happy and contented life together.

They were together at Middleton for three years, during which time Ray published his *Collection of English Words,* (p.69) and a small dictionary in three languages, (p.69) partly for the benefit of the Willughby children.

Willughby's zoological notes had not been left in a suitable state for publishing, and Ray felt that it was his duty to his late friend to see that his work was published. With characteristic generosity, he dropped most of his own botanical work including field trips, and concentrated on organising and writing Willughby's work. In 1675, Willughby's mother died and his widow made the Rays' situation difficult. The next year, Ray and his wife moved to Sutton Coldfield, which was only four miles away, - he still needed access to the collections, to be able to finish his work on birds and fishes. *The Ornithology,* appeared in 1676, in Latin, under Willughby's name. It was a magnificent folio with many plates of illustrations, which had been paid for by Willughby's widow. (p.47).

Ray was offered the secretaryship of the Royal Society in 1677 but felt that he was unable to accept, and later in the year moved to Faulkbourne Hall in Essex, only a few miles from his mother. During his two years there he produced an English version of Willughby's *Ornithology,* and second editions of both his *Catalogus Angliae,* and *English Proverbs.*

In the spring of 1679, Ray's mother died, a loss he must have felt deeply. After dealing with her affairs, Ray and his wife moved into Dewlands, their first permanent home, where Ray was to live for the rest of his life. Though he still felt his obligation to Willughby, and the fishes had yet to be completed, Ray managed to find some time for botanical writing and in 1682 published his masterpiece on classification: *Methodus Plantarum Nova.* (p.33).

Two years later it was his wife's turn to produce something, and their twin daughters Margaret and Mary arrived. Eighteen months afterwards in 1686, Willughby's *Historia Piscium* (History[17] of Fishes) at last saw the light of day, having been finished by Ray three years before. (p.51). With its completion, Ray was satisfied that his obligation to Willughby had been honoured. He could then turn to his major interest, an account of all the plants of the world. The incredible story of his massive achievement in writing and publishing his greatest work, the *Historia Plantarum,* in three volumes, in 1686, 1688 and 1704 is given in full in chapter 4. His other two daughters Catharine and Jane appeared in 1687 and 1689. The plan in the Ray household in those years, appears to have been a book one year and a daughter the next.

The 'smiling' engraving of Ray. By Lely, engraved by Meyer.
It is almost certainly from the original by Faithorne.
From *The Englishwomans Magazine*, May 1847, illustrating
an article on Ray by Mrs J.H.Pattison, who at that time was
living in Ray's old home – Dewlands, at Black Notley.

During the last years of his life, Ray was in poor health; he was often only able to work for two hours a day, and was more or less confined to the house. Despite this, he managed to maintain his incredible volume of output almost to the end, both in new works and in revisions and new editions of older ones. To give some idea of this output, the major new works only, are listed below in chronological order:

1688	*Fasciculus Stirpium Britannicarum*	(p.41)
1690	*Synopsis Methodica Stirpium Britannicarum*	(p.41)
1691	*The Wisdom of God*	(p.71)
1692	*Miscellaneous Discourses*	(p.61)
1693	*Synopsis of Animals and Reptiles*	(p.53)
1696	*Brief Dissertation*	(p.45)
1700	*Persuasive to a Holy Life*	(p.75)
1703	*Methodus Emendata*	(p.45)
1704	*Historia Plantarum* Vol. III.	(p.39)
Posthumous		
1710	*Historia Insectorum*	(p.57)
1713	*Synopsis of Birds and Fishes*	(p.59)

Ray died on 17 January 1705, and was buried in Black Notley churchyard - he was too humble to feel that he should have been buried inside the church. A memorial was built in his honour, and it is significant of the high esteem in which he has always been held, that it has not been allowed to fall into disrepair.

His library was found to contain some 1,500 volumes, mostly botanical, and was sold by auction in London two years later.

NOTES TO CHAPTER 1

1. In the first half of his life, Ray spelled his name Wray. He dropped the 'W' in 1670 and in most of his books various latin forms of Ray are used. e.g. Raii, Raji, Raio, Raium, and Joannes Raius.
2. C.E. Raven, 1942. *John Ray Naturalist*. p.3.
3. It is still very much in use as a domestic garage.
4. Some of the most vivid memories of my own childhood are of the local blacksmith at Chipping Hill in Witham (just a few miles from Black Notley), shaping red-hot iron into horse-shoes, the hiss of the plunge into cold water, and the subsequent fitting to the feet of enormous cart-horses.
5. W. Derham, 1760. *Select Remains of the Learned John Ray*. pp.52-3.
6. Raven, 1942, p.14.
7. A debate or discussion in which parties formally sustain, attack and defend a question or thesis.
8. *Select Remains*, p.3.
9. Subsizar - student receiving an allowance from the college.
10. *Select Remains*, p.4.
11. Idem, pp.6-7.
12. Quoted in Pattison, 1847, pp.259-60.
13. He does not say whether this was necessity, or just using his time to the full, by studying the contents of the cart.
14. See pp.31, 61 and 73 for details of Ray's 'Observations'.
15. J.G. Crowther, 1960. *Founders of British Science*, p.111.
16. Raven, 1941, p.4
17. *Historia* is often translated as 'History'. Though this may be correct, in many cases when used in the title of a book it should be translated as 'Account' or 'Narrative'.

A Wedgewood Portrait – Medallion of John Ray.
After a medal struck to commemorate his death, attributed
to G. Gaab. and showing him at the age of 77.
From an original in Nottingham Castle Museum.

15

THE INSCRIPTION ON RAY'S MEMORIAL AT BLACK NOTLEY CHURCH.

A translation of the Latin inscription by the Reverend William
Coyte, taken from the *Transations of the Essex Field Club*, **4**.
1886, pp. clxiii-iv.

      –   John Ray, Master of Arts,
Once Fellow of Trinity College in Cambridge.
           Afterwards
  A member of the Royal Society in London;
   And to both of these learned bodies
        An illustrious Ornament.
Hid in this narrow tomb, this marble span,
Lies all that death could snatch from this great man.
His body moulders in its native clay;
While o'er wide worlds his Works their beams display
As bright and everlasting as the day.
To those just fame ascribes immortal breath,
And in his Writings he outlives his death.
Of every Science every part he knew,
Like Solomon (and Solomon alone
We as a greater King of knowledge own)
Our modern Sage dark Nature's Secrets read
From the tall Cedar to the hyssop's bed:
From the unwieldiest Beast of land or deep,
To the least insect that has power to creep.
Nor did his artful labours only shew
Those plants which on the earth's wide surface grew,
But piercing ev'n her darkest entrails through,
All that was wise, all that was great, he knew,
And nature's inmost gloom made clear to common view.
From foreign stores his learning bright supplies,
Exposing treasures hid from others' eyes,
Loading his single mind to make his country wise.
But what's yet more, he was so Meekly great,
That envy unrepining saw his state;
For, rare accomplishments! his humble mind
Possess'd a jewell, which it could not find.
A great descent lent nothing to his fame;
Virtue, not birth, distinguished his name,
Titles and wealth he never strove to gain,
Those he would rather merit than obtain.
His private life in humble shades he spent,
Worthy a palace, with a cell content.
Unwearied he would knowledge still pursue,
The only thing in which no mean he knew.
What more did add to these bright gifts, we find
A pure untainted Piety of mind.
England's blest Church engross'd his zealous care,
A truth his dying accents did declare.
Thus lost he in retirement his great breath;
Thus dy'd he living, who thus lives in death.
Thus heav'n called his age's glory home,
And the bright wonder of the age to come.

           *   *   *

The John Ray Memorial at Black Notley Church. The tomb to the
left is that of his friend Benjamin Allen, the Braintree doctor.
An engraving showing the Linnaean Club visiting on July 3, 1844.
The original is in the Library, Royal Botanical Gardens, Kew.

CHAPTER 2

THE SCIENTIFIC BACKGROUND

A desire to classify the world about him by grouping objects into categories or classes has probably been a human characteristic since time immemorial, and as Briggs and Walters (1982) point out, there are very good reasons why man needed to differentiate between edible and poisonous plants and harmless and dangerous animals. There has been little disagreement over the desirability, even the necessity, of doing this, but for many centuries arguments have continued as to how it should be done, what criteria should be used and indeed what the purpose of such a classication should be. One of Ray's greatest achievements was to lay the foundations of a true and natural classification both in botany and zoology. In order to obtain a proper appreciation of his contribution to this area, it is necessary to look at an outline of the development of biological science prior to the state in which he found it and to look at the work of some of his predecessors.

In his 1910 work on the classification of mammals, Gregory propounded a framework which puts Ray's work in perspective between prehistoric man and Darwin. As much of this is relevant to the rest of zoology and to botany it is tabulated here and it is interesting to note that Ray is given an epoch to himself on the basis of his work on mammals alone.

I   THE PRE-SCIENTIFIC PERIOD.
II   THE GRAECO-SCHOLASTIC PERIOD.
     1. The Aristotelian Epoch.
     2. The Scholastic Epoch.
III THE MODERN PERIOD.
     1. The Renaissance Epoch.
     2. **The Raian Epoch.**
     3. The Linnean Epoch.
     4. The pre-Cuvierian Epoch.
     5. The Epoch of Cuvier and de Blainville.
     6. The Epoch of Darwin and Huxley.

THE PRE-SCIENTIFIC PERIOD.

For most of his existence man has looked at the world about him from a self-centred viewpoint. This is exemplified in astronomy in his geocentric vision of the earth as the centre of the universe with the sun orbiting the earth, and in biology in his anthropocentric attitude to plants and animals i.e. distinguishing those which are useful to him as food, medicine, tools, building materials, clothing or as religious or sacred symbols, from those that are not. Early primitive hunter-gathering societies may well have been familiar with the life cycles of various local plants, their edible parts and when and where to gather them, but from the evidence of modern primitive societies it can be deduced that they lacked any word for the concept of plant. An example of an early anthropocentric classification is given in the bible: (Leviticus 11) in which animals are classed as clean (may be eaten) or unclean (may not be eaten), on the basis of whether or not they have cloven hoofs and chew the cud.

As a by-product of this usage, early civilizations imported plants from other countries and attempts to propagate these led to the formation of gardens, originally for utilitarian purposes but later secondarily for pleasure. An Egyptian Third Dynasty grave inscription of about 3,000 B.C. illustrates a garden

containing a rectangular pond with water-lilies, surrounded by
flower-beds and trees enclosed within a wall. The cult of the
garden assumed such importance with Assyrian, Babylonian[1] and
Persian kings that the modern word for the Persian equivalent of
their heavenly pleasure gardens has entered many languages as
paradise or park.

In the pre-scientific period therefore the main emphasis was
on utilitarian use to man and it was not until the time of
Aristotle and Theophrastus that biology started as a science.

THE ANCIENT GREEKS
Aristotle (384-322 B.C.) Father of Scientific Classification.

In his *Historia animalium* (Account of Animals) Aristotle
incorporated all that was known from his predecessors and made
many significant advances. A major step was that knowledge was
sought for its own sake and that observations he had made
himself were incorporated. His *De partibus animalium* (The parts
of animals) established the groups we now know as vertebrates
and invertebrates and within the vertebrates he distinguished
birds and fishes and on the basis of either live birth or
egg-producing he separates the hairy ones (mammals) from the
cold-blooded egg-laying ones (amphibians and reptiles).

He dealt with comparative anatomy, reproduction, behaviour
and the ecology of animals and though it was not one of his aims
to produce a classification of animals that could be used for
identifications[2] he put the concept of species (individual
kinds) and genera (collective groups) on a formal basis and laid
the foundations for most of the separate divisions of biology as
we know them today. He also saw the need for names for the
different natural groups of animals and placed emphasis on the
significance of feet and teeth as important characters in
classification - a hint that other workers including Ray were to
follow later. Though Aristotle's greatest claim to fame perhaps
lies in his other works, e.g. in metaphysics, rhetoric and
logic, so great was the authority behind his name, it gave a
considerable impetus to the revival of zoology in the late
Middle Ages and Renaissance when his works were re-discovered.

There is abundant evidence in quotations from other writers
that Aristotle also thought and wrote on plants, and though his
writings on plants have been lost; it is fortunate that those of
his pupil and collaborator Theophrastus, have survived.
Theophrastus[3] (371-287 B.C.) The Father of Botany (Linnaeus).

Theophrastus's claim to fame lies in his two great works that
first put Botany on a scientific footing: *Historia Plantarum*
(Account of Plants) and *Causae Plantarum* (Origins of Plants). He
looked at the distinctive characters and nature of plants from a
morphological viewpoint, their behaviour related to their
environment, their methods of reproduction and their life
cycles. He grew many plants in a private botanical garden of
which over 500 species can be recognised today from his
descriptions; as with Ray later, he had studied the extant
literature extensively, was able to summarize previous
knowledge, add his own observations and synthesize it into a
coherent theoretical logical framework.

The *Enquiry* deals mainly with morphology, classification,
plant descriptions and economic uses, while the *Causes* deals
with reproduction and physiological topics such as plant growth.
In his classification he divides plants into four groups based
on the main criterion of "form of growth": Trees, Shrubs,

Under-shrubs and Herbs. He realized the overlapping of these
groups, and in his search for a more rational classification, he
identified many characteristics that are now of importance in
modern classification and suggested distinctions such as
flowering and flowerless plants. In his descriptions of species
he shows great originality and accuracy and he also coined an
extensive vocabulary of technical descriptive terms. In his
teachings he emphasized and exemplified the importance of direct
observation and investigation. After Theophrastus, botany in
common with all the other natural sciences, entered into a
decline and remained almost forgotten for some 1,500 years.
Interest however in the medical uses of plants remained, largely
due to the work of Dioscorides.
Dioscorides (ca 60 A.D.)
    Dioscorides, who is thought to have been a Greek physician
with the Roman army, produced his famous *Materia Medica* in about
60 A.D. In this work on drugs of use to man he had about 1,000
entries with some 500-600 derived from plants. It was structured
in a new, logical manner on the basis of the pharmacological
action of the drugs, an arrangement that made it of great
practical help to doctors. He also provided the local names for
plants, Greek and Latin synonyms and in many cases the local
names from many other countries. Though it contained virtually
no scientific botany as such, it became and remained
pre-eminent in its field for many centuries until the time of
the Renaissance. Apart from its obvious merits described above,
Morton (1981, p.68) attributes its subsequent success to the
authorititive approval given to it by Galen (A.D. 129-199), a
famous Greek physician and medical writer, and to the later
addition of illustrations of most of the plants.
    The writings of Aristotle, Theophrastus and Dioscorides,
though largely forgotten for centuries, remained the major
biological works until the Renaissance.

THE RENAISSANCE.
    As far as biology is concerned the Renaissance was a period
characterized by exploration, discovery, the collection of
natural history specimens and the rapid spread of knowledge
through printed books. The works of the ancient Greeks had
re-appeared and were translated, printed, and distributed; many
new finds in the plant world were made, herbals written and the
science of biology, particularly in botany, made great advances.
In botany, for medical uses, there was a great need for accurate
identifications and in addition, because of the large numbers of
different kinds of plant, there was a need to be able to
classify them. The establishment of herbaria and private gardens
also facilitated botanical studies. By way of contrast, in
zoology there was far less need for identification and
classification as there were far fewer known forms and there was
also less incentive to do so due to their much greater
complexity. The rest of this chapter looks at some of those
whose contributions to biology were known to John Ray.

ADVANCES IN THE SCIENCE OF BIOLOGY.
Gesner (1516-1565)
    A Swiss with an encyclopaedic knowledge based on a detailed
study of the works of an estimated two hundred and fifty authors
who preceded him, Gesner wrote books on medicine, mineralogy,
botany and zoology. In zoology his *Historia Animalium* (1551-

1558) was a massive compilation of all that had been observed and written about animals. He made considerable advances in separating fact from fiction and his illustrations, accompanied by extensive descriptions, provided the basis for future systematic workers. At the time of his death he had completed a considerable proportion of a complementary work on a general history of plants which included 1,500 drawings showing among other features great details of the flower, fruit and seed of each plant. Unfortunately much of his botanical writing was never published and it was not until the 18th century that the first of his drawings were printed. (Many have only just appeared within the last decade). Fortunately however his correspondence contained much of his thinking and from this it is evident that he had a clear idea of the modern concept of a genus being divided into two or more species. In this he may have influenced Ray who was conversant with his correspondence.

Lobelius* (de l'Obel) (1538-1616)

Though born on the continent much of his work was in England where he published his *Stirpium adversaria nova* (New day-book of plants) in 1570-71 with a revised version in 1576. His main claim to fame is that he made one of the first steps towards a natural system of plant classification. In his works he suggested that general habit, the type of growth of the whole plant or the flower and in particular differences in the leaves, should be the basis of classification. He was successful in establishing some reasonably natural groupings, he made a partial separation between the two classes now known as monocotyledons and dicotyledons and he appreciated that a fully natural classification could reveal a unity in all living organisms.

Cesalpino (1519-1603)

The driving force behind much botanical work of the period was the need for accurate identifications. To help meet this need, the science of plant classification or systematics was developed and the Italian Cesalpino made one of the first great advances in his *De Plantis libri XVI* published in Florence in 1583. In the dedication, he acknowledges his debt to Theophrastus and states that as science consists of grouping together like things and separating unlike things, he has tried to do this in his general history of plants by dividing things into classses based on characters. Book 1 is the most important and in it he gives an account of the principles of Botany and of a system of classification which is used in the remaining 15 books containing descriptions of some 1500 plants.

Many earlier workers had relied solely on books for their information. In Cesalpino's work it is abundantly clear that personally he was deeply involved in collecting, examining, describing and growing plants and that much of his data came from first hand observations. He made contributions in plant physiology and anatomy, recognizing for example the root and stem as the two fundamental parts of higher plants; he described with great accuracy the different types of leaf arrangements on plants (phyllotaxy), and the germination and structure of seeds.

In the chapters dealing with the classification of plants, he clearly establishes that he is looking for a natural classification i.e. he rejects artificial groupings such as the medical uses of Dioscorides, the alphabetical sequences of many authors or those based on what are called accidental characters (such as smell, taste, colour or habitat) and features that can

21

vary with climate or soil such as size. A natural classification
he wrote, is one which is based on the fundamental unvarying
morphological characters of the plants themselves. His search
for such a system was not only because he thought it more
scientific but because in practice it was more useful for
classifying larger numbers of plants. In defining his principles
he postulated that all organs and parts of plants can be used in
classification and for the higher classes he advocated the
characteristics of the fruit and seed as the main features to
use.

In applying his principles to his descriptions he achieved a
remarkable result in that he established a large number of
natural groupings, not only of species within genus as these
terms are used today, but also of genera within many modern
families such as Ranunculaceae (Buttercup Family), Primulaceae
(Primrose Family) and Rosaceae (Rose Family). In establishing
the concept of a natural classification, and in developing and
applying it, Cesalpino was the outstanding botanist of the
sixteenth century, though much of his work was not appreciated
till the time of Ray nearly 100 years later.

Jean Bauhin (1541-about 1605)

Bauhin was a French doctor who had studied botany in Germany
under Fuchs and accompanied Gessner on botanical journeys in the
Alps. His major work *Historia Plantarum Universalis* (Account of
Plants of the World) was not finished when he died but it was
completed and published in 1650-1651. It was the greatest work
so far published in botany and *'it contained almost everything
that is worthy of record in both ancient and modern writings
together with synonyms and critical comment.'* Ray, quoted in
(Ewen and Prime, 1975 p.33).

Gaspard Bauhin (1560-1624) (Brother of Jean)

By the beginning of the sixteenth century up to 1,000 plants
were included in herbals, many differing names had been given to
the same species by different authors, identifications were
confused and nomenclature was chaotic. The younger Bauhin
brought order to this chaos with the publication of his *Pinax
Theatri Botanici* in 1623, in which he gives names for each of
some 6,000 species and full details of the names in earlier
literature with which each was synonymous. In his nomenclature
he made considerable advances in both convenience and clarity as
for most species he used descriptive binomial names comprising a
generic name followed by a specific name, e.g. his name for the
potato: *Solanum tuberosum* which is still in use today. Ray
adopted his nomenclature and though his use of specific names
differs from that of Linnaeus, he undoubtedly influenced
Linnaeus who later proposed the adoption of binary names.

Jung (1587-1657) Professor of Natural Science at Hamburg.

Though he did not write extensively on plants, he has had
great influence due to two small publications based on his
lectures which were edited and published posthumously by two of
his former students. The most important of these, *Isagogue
Phytoscopica* (A guide to examining plants) was published in
1679, though manuscript copies were in circulation prior to this
and Ray is known to have seen one in 1660.

Jung started where Cesalpino left off and applied
mathematical methods to the analysis of the comparative
morphology of higher plants. He divided the plant into a number
of fundamental parts or organs, defined their inter-
relationships and most significantly, he devised a new logical

descriptive terminology of great practical application. His methods and terminology, which were exemplified by reference to named plants, were so sound that they were adopted later by both Ray and Linnaeus.

THE HERBALISTS.
Introduction.
To appreciate the fundamental nature of herbals it is helpful to look at the medical theory[5] behind them. This theory, which was derived from classical ideas, postulated that man's health was dependent on the correct balance of four "humours": blood, phlegm, choler and melancholy. Each "humour" corresponded to one of the elements: fire, air, water and earth and had two main characteristics in varying degrees: dryness or moistness and coldness or heat. Choler for example corresponded to fire and was dry and hot, while its opposite "humour" phlegm corresponded to water and was moist and cold. Human sickness was caused by an inbalance in the "humours" but fortunately nature had provided for this by endowing plants with "humours" also; the "humour" in a plant counteracting the opposite "humour" causing the human sickness. The physician therefore needed to diagnose accurately the disease and to identify the herb with the correct antidote in the form of the opposite "humour", which also had to be present in the correct degree or intensity. Hence the need for herbals, the primary functions of which were to give means of plant identification, details of the plant's "humour" and its intensity and the appropriate diseases it could treat.

Early herbals such as *The Grete Herball* of 1526 were full of inaccuracies, astrology, superstition, and grossly distorted illustrations; they contained horrific recipes, and were mainly culled from earlier works rather than written from direct observation. This situation was changed by William Turner.
Turner (1508-1568) The Father of British Botany and Ornithology.
Turner[6], whose life has certain parallels with that of Ray, was educated in medicine at Cambridge where, as a relaxation, he studied botany and hunted plants. He also travelled extensively on the continent and met other naturalists including Gesner. He wrote two small botanical works but his greatest was *A New Herball* published in three parts in 1551, 1562 and 1568. In the first two volumes he describes all plants known to the Greeks and Romans and the third is devoted to those discovered since then. He made many original observations and as he regarded it as his national duty to enable English physicians to know their herbs, he wrote in English and went to great lengths to provide good descriptions, locality details, and accurate names in English, Latin, Greek, German and French, which had not been done before. He is credited with providing the names in English for the first time of many plants and his herbal contains the first scientific record of some 238 native species. For the illustrations he used some four hundred high-quality wood-cut blocks, formerly used in a herbal by the German Fuchs. His book became the standard botanical medical text for many years.

He also contributed to zoology in his book on birds *Avium praecipuarum, quarum apud Plinium et Aristotelem mentio est, brevis et succincta historia* (1544). In this pioneering work he attempted to classify and identify all the species described by Aristotle and Pliny. He gave clear descriptions of living birds, corrected many previous errors, gave details of thirty seven British birds for the first time and though he followed an alphabetical sequence he gave a general classification based on morphology, habitat and food. It was the first English book solely devoted to birds.

Gerard (1545-1612)

The *Herball* or *Generall Historie of Plants* produced by the English barber-surgeon Gerard in 1597, became the most famous herbal of the period simply on the basis of its great literary merit. Though he grew many plants in his own garden near Holborn and made some original observations, most of the work, which he claimed as his own, was plagiarised from other authors. Lobelius found over 1,000 errors in it, scientifically it was confused and full of false claims, and he made many blunders due to his ignorance of Latin. (Raven, 1942 p.74) Its subsequent botanical importance is due to its revision in a second edition by Thomas Johnson in 1633.

Johnson (About 1605-1644)

Johnson, a London apothecary, published in 1629 an account of botanical journeys[7] in Hampstead Heath and Kent with lists of the plants found. This was an important historical landmark as it was the first British local flora. He made other journeys later and listed about 700 species of which he contributed some 170 first British records in his *Mercurius Botanicus* of 1634-1641.(Gilmour and Walters, 1954, p.9) Though he planned a complete work covering all British plants, this was never realized due to his early death in the civil war. His best known contribution is his edition of Gerard's *Herbal* which, with the help of his friends Goodyer and Bowles, (the latter was to help Ray later), he enlarged, improved, corrected, re-organized and published in 1633 with a reprint in 1636. Though his edition still contained many defects it was a great advance and was the one that was used by Ray.

Parkinson (1567-1650)

Botanist to Charles I and a famous gardener, Parkinson produced his first book, *Paradisi in Sole Paradisus terrestris* (The Park on Earth of the Park in sun), the title of which is a pun on his own name, in 1629. It is regarded as the first English gardening book. His second work, a herbal with the title *Theatrum Botanicum* (The Theatre of Plants), was published in 1640, and aimed at giving an account of all known plants classified on the basis of their uses and qualities. It incorporates all of Bauhin's *Pinax* and many manuscript notes made by de l'Obel and it was certainly studied in detail by Ray when he was writing his Cambridge Catalogue. In it he recorded 28 new British species for the first time, including the famous lady's slipper orchid (*Cypripedium calceolus*) found in Lancashire. (Gilmour and Walters, 1954, p.10).

NOTES TO CHAPTER 2.
1. The Hanging [= terraced] Gardens of Babylon were one of the seven wonders of the ancient world.
2. See Mayr (1981) chapter 4 for a modern view of the difference between identification and classification.
3. For a detailed account of the contribution to botany made by Theophrastus,see Morton (1981) chapter 2.
4. The genus *Lobelia* is named after Lobelius.
5. See Hoeniger and Hoeniger (1969) pp. 12-14.
6. For a full treatment of Turner see Raven (1947), pp. 48-137.
7. *Thomas Johnson*. Available in facsimile reprint and translation, edited by J.S.L.Gilmour in 1972.

CATALOGUS
PLANTARUM
CIRCA
CANTABRIGIAM
nascentium:

In qua exhibentur
Quotquot hactenus inventæ sunt, quæ
vel sponte proveniunt, vel in
agris seruntur;

Unà cum
Synonymis selectioribus, locis natalibus
& observationibus quibusdam
oppidò raris.

Adjiciuntur in gratiam tyronum,
Index Anglo-latinus, Index locorum,
Etymologia nominum, & Explicatio
quorundam terminorum.

CANTABRIGIÆ:
Excudebat *Joann. Field*, celeberrimæ
Academiæ Typographus.
Impensis Gulielmi Nealand, *Bibliopolæ.*
Ann. Dom. 1660.

CHAPTER 3

BEGINNINGS IN BOTANY

THE CAMBRIDGE CATALOGUE

In February 1660 a small, anonymous, unpretentious, pocket-sized volume was published in Cambridge. This event was to change the life of its author, the course of botanical history and start a new era in biological science. Priced at 2s 6d[1] Ray's *Catalogus Plantarum circa Cantibrigiam nascentium* (Catalogue of Cambridge Plants) appeared on the market. As Raven (1942, p.81) commented:

'Few books of such compass have contained so great a store of information and learning or exerted so great an influence upon the future.'

The author tells in his preface[2] how he came to field botany and then to write this remarkable little book:

'First I was fascinated and then absorbed by the rich spectacle of the meadows in spring-time; then I was filled with wonder and delight by the marvellous shape, colour and structure of the individual plants.

While my eyes feasted on these sights, my mind too was stimulated. I became inspired with a passion for Botany, and I conceived a burning desire to become proficient in that study, from which I promised myself much innocent pleasure to soothe my solitude.'

On looking for advice and guidance in the University he was astonished to find that there was no one who could give him any help. Not to be dissuaded he decided that this essential branch of Natural Philosophy, should not remain neglected, when he, with ample leisure and moderate attainments, could benefit both the University and others who wished to study Botany, while at the same time enjoying a congenial pursuit.

He started by collecting simples (medicinal plants) and planting them in the garden outside his room at Trinity College; then he went on long walks around Cambridge collecting and observing as many different plants as he could find. His method of study as outlined in the preface[2] is still highly relevant today:

'First of all I had to familiarise myself with the literature of the subject, and then compared the plants that I had found in the countryside with the pictures in the books; then when I found any similarity between them, I had to study the descriptions more closely. After a time I acquired skill from practice; when I chanced upon some unknown plant, I first considered to what tribe and family it belonged or could be assigned (after I had been occupied some time with Phytology, I developed a facility in identifying the points of similarity) so I first of all looked for it in the appropriate group, and in this way saved myself a great deal of trouble.'

The best way, he felt, of helping the studies of others would be to publish a Catalogue of all the plants he had found in the area. From when he first started he spent six years collecting, observing and making notes, followed by a further three years of writing and revising. He modestly points out that even with taking great care mistakes may occur and he promises:[2]

'I will be more careful in future not to submit anything that has not been subject to the most careful and prolonged review, for I have allowed a measure of haste to enter into the present work by my desire to breathe new life as quickly as possible into the almost extinct and moribund study of Botany.'

He acknowledges the help and support given to him by his
great friends John Nidd, Francis Willughby and Peter Courthope
and emphasises that his aims were:[2]
*'to illustrate the glory of God in the knowledge of the
works of Nature or Creation, then to enhance the fame of my Alma
Mater, the University of Cambridge, which must suffer in public
esteem if it should appear deficient in this field of learning.'*
    The composition of the book is interesting in that it
contains eight sections. After the preface (16pp.) he gives a
bibliography (12pp.) of about 50 reference works. He had not
seen all of these but for many he gives details including
critical comment, indicating his very wide range of reading and
comprehension. The catalogue which follows (182pp.), lists
alphabetically, 671[3] plants. In explaining his method of working
and the rules he applies, he states that whenever possible he
uses the names taken from Jean and Gaspard [=Caspar] Bauhin,
Gerard and Parkinson. If early descriptions are not clear he
uses a collection of descriptive synonyms, each followed by an
abbreviated author's name. e.g. the plant we know as Fine-leaved
Water Dropwort [=*Oenanthe aquatica* (L.)] is listed on page 34
as: Cicutaria palustris *Lob.Ger.* palustris tenuifolia *Park.C.B.*
Phellandrium *Plinii Dod.Lugd.* Phellandrium vel Cicutaria
aquatica quorundam *J.B.* Though the catalogue entries including
notes are mainly in Latin, names and localities are. given in
English: *'Marsh or water Hemlock. In the river and in great
ditches of water almost everywhere.'*
    Where a species had either not been described before or where
the descriptions were confused or obscure, he added from his own
observations accurate details of morphology, habit, whether
annual or perennial, time of flowering and medical uses where
relevant, thereby setting new high standards for descriptive
botany. English names and their Latin equivalents are given in
an index (29pp.) which has its own sub-title page and numbering.
This is followed by a summary of the major plants found in each
of seventeen localities around Cambridge e.g. for Madingley: *'In
the Wood'* and *'In the lanes and closes about the Town.'*
    The etymology of the Latin names of plants is covered in 48
pages and shows his great knowledge of Latin, Greek and Hebrew.
A sixteen-page Terminorum or explanation of some of the Latin
terms he uses is next. In this he refers to the work of Jung
which he had seen in manuscript form. The final section is a
Capita or outline classification of plants of just over three
pages, which as Raven (1942 p.108) points out, was derived from
Bauhin's *Historia Universalis Plantarum*. Ray's use of an
alphabetical classification throughout, indicates that he did
not regard Bauhin's work as satisfactory, even though it was the
best available at the time. His final comment that plants can be
classified by other means such as flowers, seeds and leaves is a
clear indication that he was already thinking about his great
work on classification that was yet to come.
    The Catalogue was highly significant as the first Local Flora
of any British County and in it Ray stressed that he hoped its
publication would encourage others to make similar surveys of
their own localities, so that, eventually, a complete
Phytologica Britannica or Flora of Britain could be produced.
    In his study of previous works Ray found a chaotic jumble of
synonyms, obscure descriptions, duplications and a complete lack
of species distinctions. With acute insight he realized that
before any attempt could be made at a classification of plants

it was necessary to bring some order to this chaos and to have means of accurate identification by fixing species names and descriptions. This he did by sifting data, sorting out the multiplicity of names used by different authors for the same plant (an amazing task in its own right), and producing accurate descriptions many of which were from his own observations. The great achievement of Ray's Catalogue was that he managed to do this almost unaided. At the same time he was laying the foundations of scientific botany, plant distribution and geography, entirely divorced from the astrology, alchemy, superstition and utilitarian use to man that characterized most previous works. In looking at the contents of the Catalogue, Raven (1942 p.92) summarizes his greatness in masterly fashion:
'The knowledge that he gained of the flora of Cambridgeshire would have been remarkable if he had possessed the books and collections of a modern student: considering his handicaps, the lack of any reliable authorities, the pressure of his other work and the difficulty of travel, it is evidence not only of rare energy and powers of observation, but of a genius for natural history; a flair for locality combined with a fine sense of the characteristics of plant life.'

So thorough was his work that, two hundred years later, when Babington's *Flora of Cambridgeshire* (1860) listed some 950 species, over 700 of these had been recorded by Ray.

In his *Novum Organum* of 1620 Bacon first propounded the concept of scientific investigation based on observation, experimentation and the analysis of facts, to replace the blind acceptance of written authority that had been prevalent until then. Important as was Ray's first book for botany it also has a place in the general history of science, as it exemplified this new Baconian philosophy in the tradition of Boyle's experiments with air and Hooke's discoveries with the microscope.

THE TABLE OF PLANTS

Ray's first endeavour at classification was one that was imposed on him from outside. In 1666, Bishop Wilkins a prominent member of the Royal Society, wrote to Willughby asking for his help in producing a set of tables of the families of animals and plants for a book he had written called the *Essay towards a Real Character and Philosophical Language,* This was an attempt at producing a universal language for the interchange of knowledge, to replace Latin which was passing out of vogue. In his letter he asked for Ray's help with the plants. Unfortunately only three weeks were available as the book was already being printed and Wilkins imposed an arbitrary system whereby the plants should be separated into three groups, each of nine divisions, within which the plants were to be grouped in pairs.

Ray was well aware of the ridiculous and unnatural nature of such constraints but nevertheless he managed to comply with Wilkins's request and to produce a classification that was an advance on any previous attempt. He established a number of natural groupings and points of taxonomy but when the book was published by the Royal Society in 1668 it was not successful.

Though Ray had not wasted much time on the Tables, they led the following year to an unfortunate episode in which the arrogant Robert Morison[*], in his *Praeludia Botanica* (1669), made an entirely unwarranted and savage attack on Ray's Table of classes of plants. Ray was deeply hurt but due to his dislike of controversy he did not reply publicly.

CATALOGUS
PLANTARUM
A N G L I Æ,
E T *Reddicy fid. a-u*

Infularum Adjacentium :

Tum Indigenas, tum in agris paffim cultas complectens.

In quo præter Synonyma neceffaria, facultates quoque fummatim traduntur, unà cum Obfervationibus & Experimentis Novis Medicis & Phyficis. *F. J. Voulou*

Editio fecunda, Plantis circiter quadraginta fex, & Obfervationibus aliquammultis auctior.

OPERA
JOANNIS RAII, M.A.
& Societatis Regiæ Sodalis.

LONDINI,
Typis *Andr. Clark,* Impenfis *Joh. Martyn* Regalis Societatis Typographi, ad Infigne Campanæ in Cœmeterio D.*Pauli.* M. DC. LXXVII.

THE ENGLISH CATALOGUE

In a letter to Willughby[5] accompanying a copy of the Cambridge Catalogue, Ray outlined the plans for his next work:

'You remember that we lately, out of *Gerard, Parkinson* and *Phytologia Britannica*, made a collection of rare plants, whose places are therein mentioned, and ranked them under the several counties. My intention now is to carry on and perfect that design; to which purpose I am now writing to all my friends and acquaintance who are skilled in herbary, to request them this next summer each to search diligently his country for plants, and to send me a catalogue of such as they find, together with the places where they grow. In divers counties I have such as are skilled and industrious. For **Warwickshire** and **Nottinghamshire** I must beg your assistance, which I hope,.. you will be willing to contribute. After that, partly by my own search, partly by the mentioned assistance, I shall have got as much information and knowledge of the plants of each country as I can, (which will require some years) I do design to put forward a compleat P.B. which I hope to bring into as narrow a compass as this book. First, I shall give the names of all plants that are or shall then be found growing in England in an alphabetical order, together with their synonyms, excepting such as are mentioned in this catalogue, whose synonyms I shall omit, setting down only one name, and referring for the rest to 'Cat.Cant.''

He gave further details and asked for Willughby's comments. These were obviously favourable, as over the next decade, with the exception of three years spent on the continent, Ray travelled extensively over most of Great Britain, often in the company of one or both of his friends Skippon and Willughby. The first journey was in 1660 to the north of England and the Isle of Man with Willughby; 1661 saw him in York, Edinburgh, Glasgow and Carlisle with Skippon; a tour round Wales with both Skippon and Willughby followed the next year and a similar pattern was established during 1666-1669 after his return from Europe.

Ray's time during these travels was spent in observing, examining, recording and collecting not only plants but also unusual words, proverbs and details of dialects and industrial processes. These journeys were to him what the voyage of the Beagle was to Darwin, and the incredible volume of output that poured from his pen over the rest of his life was largely based on the data collected during this period.

In 1670, ten years after work started on it, the *Catalogus Plantarum Angliae* (Catalogue of English Plants) was published. Ray, through tremendous efforts, had in effect extended his first book to cover the whole of England. With much greater experience behind him he had considerably more confidence and knowledge, resulting in many improvements over the Cambridge Catalogue both in arrangement and content. His identifications were more accurate as he had seen for himself nearly every plant included and he produced an important section devoted to the importance and definition of species. In this he stressed the need both for defining and recognizing species and then of detecting the unique medical properties of each. (He was well aware of the differing pharmacological actions of closely-related plants.)

Many entries have notes covering the medical properties of the plant concerned and he provided a large index at the back containing a list of diseases, symptoms and pharmacological

CATALOGUS
STIRPIUM
IN
Exteris Regionibus
A nobis Observatarum,

Quæ vel non omnino vel parcè admodum
IN
ANGLIA
Sponte proveniunt.

LONDINI:

Typis *Andreæ Clark*, Impensis *J. Martyn* Regalis Societatis
Typographi, apud quem prostant ad insigne Campanæ
in Cœmeterio Divi Pauli, M DC LXXIII.

actions with the appropriate plants to use for each. e.g. For
epilepsy he gives six plants[6], for angina, seven and for use as
diuretics no less than forty seven plants. As Raven (1942 p.159)
commented on his medical notes:
  *'If his efforts seem disproportionate or unnecessary, we
must remember the fantastic and horrible drugs that were still
in general use - the best doctor in Braintree regularly used
essence of woodlice and peacock's dung - and the extent to which
magic, astrology and alchemy still entered into medical practice
...it is certain that he did important service in promoting the
scientific investigation of the medical uses of plants, and in
combating its age-long association with superstition.'*
  Its accurate scientific content alone was enough to ensure
its success, and this combined with its pocket-sized portability
enabling it to be used in the field, necessitated a second
enlarged edition in 1677. (The title-page is shown on page 28.)

THE CATALOGUE OF FOREIGN PLANTS

  Until his continental tour of 1663-1666, Ray had little
direct contact with plants from outside Great Britain. For him
the tour was a marvellous opportunity to study the European
flora, meet foreign scientists and examine local collections.
Everywhere he went he made lists of the plants he found and his
delight in new discovery is well expressed in the preface:[7]
  *'Whether my readers will enjoy these bare lists of names,
I do not know: to me to gaze at the plants themselves freely
growing on the lavish bosom of mother earth was an unbelievable
delight; I can say with Clusius that I was as pleased to find
for the first time a new plant as if I had received a fortune;
to discover very many daily that were unknown to me and
strangers to our Britain was an ample reward for travel.'*
  In the preface, his main concern is to outline the criteria
that should be used to determine the distinctness of species and
in one paragraph he questions the immutability of species: 'a
true transformation of species cannot be denied unless we set
aside the evidence of first-hand and reliable witnesses'[7].
  The Catalogue itself: *Catalogus Stirpium in Exteris
Regionibus*, which was printed in Latin with its own numbering
and sub-title page (shown opposite), was not published as a
separate entity, but was bound in with an account in English of
other observations made on the tour. This was issued in 1673
with the title: *Observations Topographical, Moral, and
Physiological; Made in a Journey through part of the Low-
Countries, Germany, Italy, and France: with A Catalogue of
Plants not Native of England, found spontaneously growing in
those parts, and their Virtues*. Though the Catalogue was
basically an alphabetical list, with synonyms from the major
authors, he made a remarkable number of new European finds which
he also named and described. The botanists on the continent
recognized it as a great achievement, but as Raven (1942 p.175)
points out, the greatest effect was probably on Ray himself:
  *'He had seen a larger number of plants in their wild state
than any contemporary botanist and made himself a master of his
subject: he added a considerable number of new species to the
European flora and collated all the authorities in identifying
them: he had gained an international reputation as a scientist
and established friendly contacts with all the leaders of
learning: he was qualified for what he always regarded as his
life's work.'* A second edition was published in 1738.

METHODUS
PLANTARUM
NOVA

EXPERIMENT, CLASSIFICATION AND THE NEW METHOD OF PLANTS.
Ray's greatest and most original contribution to Botany is
generally accepted to be in the improvements he made to the
science of plant classification. His first major work in this
area was the *Methodus Plantarum Nova* (New Method of Plants)
published in 1682. This was followed by the first volume of
Historia Plantarum (1686) and *Methodus Plantarum Emendata et
Aucta* (1703) which are covered in chapter 4.

As a result of his work on the Table of Plants for Wilkins
(p.27), Ray realized that it was not sufficient to base a plant
classification on just one or two characters, (as Lobelius had
used leaves or Cesalpino the fruit and seed), but that it was
necessary to use the whole structure of the plant as far as
possible. Up until then he had been mainly a collector, observer
and collator, and in order to improve his knowledge and
understanding of plants so that he could produce the best
possible classification, he conducted experiments to learn about
their physiology and growth.

During his stay at Wollaton in the Spring of 1669 both he and
Willughby experimented, using relatively simple equipment. They
bored holes in various species of tree including Birch, Sycamore
and Willow and studied the movement of sap under different
conditions. Their results were published in the *Philosophical
Transactions* of the Royal Society in June 1669 under the title:
'*Experiments Covering the motion of the Sap in Trees, made this
Spring.*' Though their results were not outstanding and were of
no help to classification, what was particularly significant was
that this was the first recorded attempt at a systematic study
of plant physiology. (Raven, 1942 p.188). The content and
concepts of their paper represented a startling innovation and
its publication made a very favourable impression on the members
of the Royal Society, encouraged others to start experimentation
and gave a new direction and impetus to botanical science.

His next two papers were read to the Royal Society on 17th
December 1674. In the first '*On the Seeds of Plants*', he showed
that some plants have two seed-leaves; one coming from each of
the two lobes of the seed, while others only have one seed-leaf
with the seed undivided. This is now recognized as one of the
fundamental divisions in the plant world and though he did not
use the terms dicotyledon and monocotyledon in this paper, and
the full implications of his observations had not dawned on him
then, it represented a major step in plant classification.

The second paper '*On the Specific Differences of Plants*' was
also important as in it he established precise criteria for
determining what was and what was not, a species. (This applied
equally to zoology.) He listed a large number of accidental
characters including size, colour, smell, taste, shape and
variegation, explained why they were not suitable for use in
determining specific distinctions and stressed the use of
overall structural morphology as the main criterion.

Over the next five years he was involved in producing and
revising several books unrelated to botany. Though he
undoubtedly worked intermittently at his *Methodus* during this
period, it was only in the three years following the death of
his mother in 1679, when he had moved to Dewlands at Black
Notley, that he had time to return to his main interest,
classification, and to finish writing the New Method of Plants.

The *Methodus* was produced as a small slim volume with an
allegorical plate (shown opposite) preceding the title page.

34

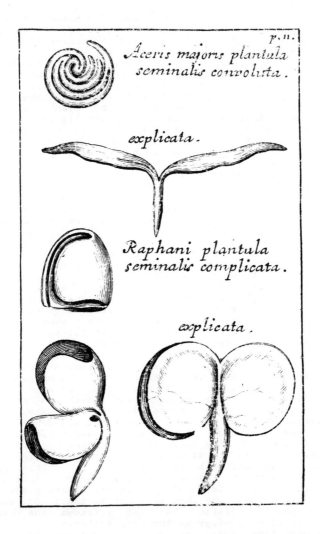

Illustration from Malpighi's *Anatomy of Plants* (1675), showing
seeds of sycamore and radish. It was used by Ray, as his only
text-illustration, in both his *New Method of Plants* (1682) and
his *History of Plants* (1686-1704).

In the preface he outlines his purpose: (Raven, 1942 p.193)
*'The number and variety of plants inevitably produce a
sense of confusion in the mind of the student: but nothing is
more helpful to clear understanding, prompt recognition and
sound memory than a well-ordered arrangement into classes,
primary and subordinate. A Method seemed to me to be useful to
botanists, especially beginners; I promised long ago to produce
and publish one, and have now done so at the request of some
friends.'*
He goes on to explain the limitations of his method and the
unfavourable circumstances under which he worked. For species
classification he uses the principal parts of the plant; flower,
calyx, seed and seed-vessel, because they are constant i.e. they
can be reproduced from seeds; and do not vary as do accidental
characters. In addition, features of these parts such as their
position, shape and number can easily be seen and used in
association with other characteristics to form groups. (genera)
    Cesalpino's work and his use of the number of seeds and
seed-vessels in classification is praised and he includes
Cesalpino's Synopsis at the end. The work of Jung, Colonna and
Morison is also mentioned but he points out that his is a new
method based on original observation and is not a compilation.
The preface also contains his first use of the word **petal**[a] for
the leaf of a flower and lists the characteristics of the main
kinds (orders) of herbs.
    Though the classification tables, of which there are eight on
trees, six on shrubs and forty-seven on herbs, comprise the main
text (pp.28-160), the five introductory essays are of greatest
interest and in particular the third: *De Plantula seminali
reliquisque semine contentis*, which explains the structure of
the seed and the embryo. In this he firmly establishes the
division between seeds with two lobes and those with only one.
i.e. the major categories of dicotyledons and monocotyledons
still used in botany today. He describes the different forms of
seeds in detail and uses as his only illustration in the text, a
plate from Malpighi's Anatomy of Plants (1675) showing seeds of
sycamore and radish. (Shown opposite.) As Raven (1942 p.195) so
aptly says *"The essay is literally an epoch-making piece of
work,"* giving the book a profound historical significance.

NOTES TO CHAPTER 3
1. [2s 6d = two shillings and sixpence or 12.5p in modern
   currency.] This price was noted inside John Goodyer's copy
   which he bought in May 1660. See Gunther (1922, pp.222-3) or
   (1928, p.15). Due to its scarcity, copies today are valued at
   some 2,000 times this amount.
2. From *Ray's Flora of Cambridgeshire*, 1975, translated and
   edited by A.H.Ewen and C.T.Prime.
3. This excludes crop plants and mosses and a few lower plants.
   An appendix was published in 1663 giving 37 new plants with a
   2nd edition in 1685 by Dent, with 59 new records.
4. For details of the Morison controversy see Raven, chapter 8.
5. See Dereham's *Philosophical Letters* p.356.
6. It is interesting to note that *Digitalis*, which is now well
   known for its use in heart disease was included here rather
   than under angina.
7. Translated by Raven (1942 p.174)
8. The word *petal* had been suggested earlier by Colonna but it
   was Ray who brought it into general use. (Morton, 1981 p.207)

HISTORIA
PLANTARUM

Species hactenus editas aliafque infuper multas
noviter inventas & defcriptas complectens.

In qua agitur primò

De Plantis in genere,

Earúmque

PARTIBUS, ACCIDENTIBUS & DIFFERENTIIS;

Deinde

Genera omnia tum fumma tum fubalterna ad Species ufque infimas,

Notis fuis certis & Characteriflicis

Definita,

METHODO

Naturæ veftigiis infiftente difponuntur;

Species fingulæ accurate defcribuntur, obfcura illuftrantur,
omiffa fupplentur, fuperflua refecantur, Synonyma neceffaria
adjiciuntur;

VIRES denique & USUS
recepti compendiò traduntur.

AUCTORE

JOANNE RAIO,

E Societate Regiâ, & SS. Individuæ Trinitatis *Collegii apud* Cantabrigienfes
quondam Socio.

TOMUS PRIMUS.

LONDINI:

Typis MARIÆ CLARK: Proftant apud HENRICUM FAITHORNE
Regiæ Societatis Typographum, ad Infigne Rofæ in Cœmeterio D. *Pauli,* cIↃ IↃ cLxxxvi.

Title-page of Volume I of Ray's most famous work -
History of Plants (1686).

CHAPTER 4

THE HISTORY OF PLANTS and LATER BOTANICAL STUDIES

THE HISTORY OF PLANTS

Ray's most famous work was undoubtedly his *Historia Plantarum* (History of Plants) published in three volumes in 1686, 1688 and 1704. It was not only intellectually 'great' but also physically, both from the immense labour that went into it and the statistics of the three massive folio volumes (each about 8kg) with a total of over 2,600 pages of small type, each page measuring some 45cm by 28cm.

His aims in producing his *magnum opus* are outlined in a letter[1] he wrote to Sloane[2] in 1784:

'1. To satisfy the importunity of some friends who solicited me to undertake it. 2. To give some light to young students in the reading and comparing other herbarists, by correcting mistakes, and illustrating what is obscure...3. To alleviate the charge of such as are not able to purchase many books; to which end I will endeavour an enumeration of all the species already described and published. 4. To facilitate the learning of plants, if need be, without a guide or demonstrator, by so methodizing of them, and giving such certain and obvious characteristic notes of the genera, that it shall not be difficult for any man ..to find out infallibly any plant that shall be offered to him, especially being assisted by the figure of it.'

He also gave as another reason the fact that no Englishman since Turner the previous century (see p.22), had attempted such a task.

It was not to be just an alphabetical catalogue of British and European plants but was to contain, as far as possible, descriptions of all known plants of the world, arranged in an updated and expanded version of his Method.

Ray originally started on the History at Willughby's suggestion but he gave up after Willughby's death in 1675 when he discovered that Dr Morison was working on similar lines. Morison died in 1683 leaving most of his work incomplete. Ray was then persuaded by his friends, especially Charles Hatton, to whom the *Historia* is dedicated, to resume work. The amazing achievement of Volume I alone and the circumstances of its production have been summarized by Raven: (1942, pp.216-7).

'This first volume, a very large folio, containing 22 unnumbered and 984 numbered pages,.... is one of those works which by their sheer mass and magnitude create a sense of awe. In these days of small books and co-operative effort it seems hardly credible that such a tome can be the product of a single author and three years of writing. As one studies the endless series of descriptions, the multitude of references, the concentrated attention bestowed upon each separate species, and the innumerable points of detail discussed in the appended notes, the impression is deepened..If he had lived in a cloister or a library, the work would still have been heroic: he did it in a cottage with few books, dependent upon a rather unreliable carrier and on the good offices of friends in London: he was nearly sixty, already in indifferent health, and the four baby girls were born during its production. There have been giants in the earth: and on the evidence of these books Ray would have a claim to stand among them.'

The *Historia* did contain descriptions of all known plants, those which were provided by Ray being given in considerable

38

Lib. XXVIII.   *De Arboribus Bacciferis.*   1617

haud videtur, quòd in quibufdam ægris aphthofa crufta non craffa linguæ & palato adeò pertinaciter adhæret, ut lenientibus gargarifmatis fcil. à decocto Raparum, Hordei, &c. quæ contra Aphthas maximè conducunt, intra paucos dies abftergeri haud potuerat, ægri licet à febre immunes effent, brevi tamen fugatur potu vini Gallici: quia particulæ aphthofæ fubinde acriore ftimulo ad fui liberationem egent.

Genera vini Veteribus celebrata recenfet Plinius lib. 14. c. 6. D. Auguftus (inquit) Setinum cunctis prætulit, & fecuti Principes, confeffa propter experimenta, &c. Nafcitur fupra forum Appii [Setia oppidum eft in colle à Terracina quinque millibus diffitum; hodie *Sezza*] Antea Cæcubo erat generofitas, celeberrima in paluftribus Populetis, finu Amyclano, quod jam intercidit & incuria coloni, locíque anguftiâ, magis tamen foffâ Neronis, &c. Secunda nobilitas Falerno agro erat, & ex eo maximè Fauftiano. Exolefcit quoque hoc copiæ potiùs quam bonitati ftudentium. Falernus ager à ponte Campano læva petentibus urbanam coloniam Syllanam, nuper Capuæ contributam incipit. Fauftianus autem circiter 4. mill. à vico prope Cedias, qui vicus à Sinueffa 6. millibus abeft: nec ulli in vino major autoritas. Solo vinorum flamma accenditur. Tria ejus genera, Aufterum, dulce, tenue. Quidam ità diftinguunt: Summis collibus Gauranum gigni, mediis Fauftianum, imis Falernum. Non omittendum autem, nulli eorum quæ celebrantur jucundum faporem uvæ effe. Ad tertiam palmam variè venére, *Albana* urbi vicina prædulcia ac rara in auftero. Item Surrentina,in vineis tantùm nafcentia, convalefcentibus maximè probata propter tenuitatem, falubritatémque. Tib. Cæfar dicebat confenfiffe medicos ut nobilitatem Surrentino darent, alioquin effe generofum acetum. Certant Maffica æquè ex monte Gaurano Puteolos Baiafque profpectantia. Inter Græca vina maximè celebrata fuere Maroneum in Cherfonefo Thraciæ, Thafium, Creticum, Coum, Chium, Lesbium, Icarium, Smyrnæum, &c. Inter Afiatica Clazomenæ, & montis Libani vina. Reliqua genera vide apud Plinium loco citatò. Noftri enim inftituti non eft omnia vini genera quorum nomina apud Veteres & Recentiores occurrunt enumerare. Sufficiat aliqua eorum quæ apud nos hodie in ufu & pretio funt breviter indicâffe. Ea funt è Gallicis 1. Parifinum, tenue & oligophorum, ubi bene maturum grati faporis & ftudiofis aptum, *Vin de Paris, Champagne:* 2. *Campanum* omnium Gallicanorum delicatiffimum: 3. *Burdegalenfe* feu Gravianum. **Common Claret Wine, oʒ Graves Wine.** 4. Vinum *Burgundiacum,* **Burgundy Wine:** inter Burgundiaca autem primum locum obtinet Beaunenfe, fecundùm vulgare proverbium Vinum Belnenfe fuper omnia recenfe. 5. *Vinum album vulgare,* **Common White Wine.** 6. *Vinum Frontinianum,* generofiffimum & mofchum redolens. 7. *Vina Aurelianenfia* magni fiunt in Francia ob generofitatem & falubritatem. 8. **Hermitage,** Vinum Eremiticum.

Ex Hifpanicis ufitatiffima & notiffima funt, 1. Canarinum, **Canary-Sack** omnium laudatiffimum, generofum & lene, naturæ amicum. 2. *Malacenfe* vetus, **Malaga Sack,** præcedente etiam opimius & pinguius, at fi copiosè fumatur caput gravans. 3. *Xeranum,* **Sherry-Sack,** aufterius & palato minùs gratum. 4. *Alonenfe,* **Alicant Wine,** rubrum & craffum, palato quidem gratum, at ftomacho minus utile & caput gravans. Huic non multùm diffimile eft genus illud, quod noftratibus, **Tent-wine** dicitur. Nominis ratio mihi nondum cognita. Adfertur etiam ad nos ex Lufitania Vinum Portuenfe **Porto poʒt Wine,** fed rarius. Vinum Maderæ Infulæ ex majori parte in Americam transfertur. Ex Italicis pauca importantur, ex Hetruria *Vinum Florentinum rubrum,* ftomacho commodiffimum & in convictibus faluberrimum. 2. *Verdea* dictum, itidem ex Hetruria, album, dulce & lene, magis gratum palato, quam ftomacho utile. In Italia ipfa celebrantur, Venetiis *Vin. Malvaticum, Malvafia,* Canarino proximum, non in Italia natum fed in Creta infula; *Vicentinum rubrum, dolce & piccante* dictum. In Hetruria *Falifcinum* five de *monte Fiafcone* ; Romæ *Albanum* olim celebre, & de *monte Pulciano* ; *Syracufanum* ex Sicilia infula; Neapoli Vinum rubrum *Lachrymæ Chrifti* dictum, & Vinum Græcum ad radices Vefuvii montis ortum.

Vinum Mofchatellinum rubrum ex infula Creta defertur. **Red Mufcadine.**

Ex Germanicis Rhenana fola aut non procul à Rheno remotæ originis ad nosimportantur, ut Nicrinum **Neccar Wine,** Rinchovianum, Hochamore, Mofellanum, & *Baccheroe.*

Vinum autem aliis potulentis quibufcunque Cerevifiæ, Melicrato, Pomaceo, Apiiti, exterifque è fructibus factitiis tum voluptatis tum falubritatis refpectu longè antecellit. Nec dierum vina aufteriora quamvis palato minùs arrideant, ventriculo tamen commodiora & cibo concoquendo magis idonea cenfentur ; ut vina rubra Gallica & Florentina, quæ afperiufcula & ftyptica linguæ & palato fentiuntur ; quàm alba, quæ lenia & dulcia. Verùm fi omnia quæ de vinis dicta funt & adhuc dicenda reftant perfequi vellem huic foli hiftoriæ non unum fufficeret. Qui plura velit legat *Andreæ Baccii* eruditiffimum *opus* de Vini generibus Anno 1596. Romæ impreffum, in quo quicquid ab Antiquis & Recentioribus de Hiftoria Uvæ proditum occurrit complexus eft, unà cum Obfervationibus plurimis propriis & animadverfionibus in Vina Græca, Italica, Hifpanica, Gallica & Rhenana, eorundem culturas, locos, nomina, varios præparandi & tractandi modos, morbos & remedia, vaforum veterum & novorum multiplicem varietatem, cellas, &c. refpicientes.

Omphacium Veteribus noftrum erat acerbæ & nondum maturæ uvæ, Sole reficcatus & denfatus ad confiftentiam Rob. Recentioribus eft fuccus Uvæ immaturæ expreffus, colatus, in dolia reconditus, & vafe claufo affervatus. Utrumque refrigerat & ficcat ; hoc non ad medicamenta tantùm fed ad ciborum condimenta & intinctus utile eft, naufeam ac cibi faftidium tollit, appetentiam excitat, alvi fluores reprimit, ardores ftomachi aliorúnnque vifcerum mitigat, non modo intus fumptum fed & foris admotum.

Diofcoride autore, Omphacium Veterum oculorum claritati confert, eorundémque fcabritiæ & angulis arrofis, quod hodie de pomorum fylveftrium agrefta vero experimur.

Schroderus Omphacium calidis morbis omnibus feliciori juvamento effe ait quàm acetum, quod præter refrigerandi vim & caliditate acri pollet, fecus ac Omphacium.

Sapa, Græcis ἕψημα ἢ σίραιον ingenii non naturæ opus eft, mufto ufque ad tertiam partem menfuræ decocto. Plin. l. 14. c. 9. & l. 23. c. 2.

X x x x x x 3   *Defrutum*

Ray's wine list from Volume II of *Historia Plantarum.*

detail. They are spread over 125 sections, of which many correspond to modern families. In the early chapters of Volume I, he produced what was in effect a very detailed up-to date textbook of botanical science covering all that was known on anatomy, physiology, reproduction, morphology and classification.

In particular, he made full use of Jung's terminology and morphological system (see pp.27-8). He used the anatomical and physiological observations of his contemporaries Grew and Malpighi. The flower was defined in far more precise terms than had previously been done, and he laid the foundations for future studies in plant physiology. In doing so he outlined details of the movement of water as a major feature of transpiration in plants, and explained the function of the sap in providing rigidity to leaf tissue. Later, in *The Wisdom of God* (see Ch.8), from his significant interpretation of Malphigi's experiments, he showed that the main function of leaves is to make food for the fruit and the whole plant, both from the sap rising through the roots and that which came from rain, dew and the air through the leaves. He was as always, particularly generous in giving credit where it was due and in acknowledging the work of others.

Volume I includes the second of his major works on classification and in it he distinguishes between flowering and non-flowering plants as major groups. He uses the divisions of dicotyledons and monocotyledons that he had established in the *Methodus*, and indicates the differences between plants with enclosed seeds (Angiosperms) and those with naked seeds (Gymnosperms). All of these categories have major taxonomic significance in botany today. Although Theophrastus, some 2,000 years earlier, had suggested the dicotyledon/monocotyledon and enclosed/naked seed divisions, it needed someone of the stature of Ray to realise their significance and incoprorate them into a natural systematic classification. In addition he made considerable advances in dividing Ferns and Fungi into groups. The fern divisions for example, being based on the position of the seed and the type of leaf. He also made an important contribution by establishing as a main criterion for the definition of a species, the distinguishing features that arise from seeds[3]. He pointed out that one species never came from the seed of another and that this principle also applied to animals.

His own descriptions are models of clarity, brevity, and completeness. He provides synonyms and details of habitat, locality and gross morphology and notes on related species. He also covers methods of propagation and of collecting and drying plants, medicinal properties, the chemistry of plants and plant diseases. Some 6,900 species are covered in the first two volumes; of which he knew over 6,000 from first hand knowledge. Volume I deals with dicotyledons while Volume II has the last two tribes of dicotyledons, the monocotyledons and the *Dendrologia* or trees. The third volume contains at least a further 10,000 new entries, mainly compiled from works published since 1688, with plants from many parts of the world including America, Africa, the Far East, The Phillipines and the West Indies. He emphasises the term *petal*, mentioned in the *Methodus*, to distinguish the floral from the ordinary leaves and introduced the word *pollen* in its modern sense, for the small globules produced by the anthers of flowers.

Ray was not a wealthy man, and in the poor economic climate of the period, he was unable to raise funds for illustrations,

TAB. XI.   Pag. 279.

Illustration from Ray's *Flora of Britain* (1724), showing
Veronica spicata. (Ray Society facsimile, 1973).

despite an appeal at the end of Volume I. This was one of his major regrets as he felt that a work on plants without illustrations was like a geography without maps", and until the end of his life he hoped that plates could be provided. In his preparation for Volume III, Ray was helped by many friends. One in particular, James Petiver (1664?-1718), attempted to remedy this omission after Ray's death and in 1713-15 he published, partly as a tribute to Ray, an illustrated catalogue[5] with many figures on 72 engraved copper-plates.

On page 1617, in Book 28 of Volume II, Ray gives an interesting commentary on the products obtained from certain plants - wines. This is yet another example of his extraordinary breadth of interests, though he does not say to what extent his knowledge is first-hand. Raven, (1942 pp.241-2) gives a full translation of his wine list, and the original is reproduced here in reduction (see p. 38), to give an indication of the amount of information on one page and of the incredible labour that went into writing the three volumes.

In the *Historia*, Ray shows his genius for abstracting and summarizing the best of all that had gone before him, coupling it with his own massive and unique contribution and synthesizing it into a coherent whole; resulting in a clear, succinct and masterly exposition of current botanical knowledge, both theoretical and experimental; thereby laying one of the great foundation stones on which modern botanical science is based.

THE FASCICULUS OF BRITISH PLANTS

Ray had hoped that a third edition of his Catalogue of English Plants would be published after the second edition had sold out. Though he had corrections and many new species ready, this never appeared due to problems with his printers. Instead, his additional material in the form of a supplement of English plants, was published by Martyn[6] the new printer to the Royal Society. It was issued in 1688 with the title *Fasciculus Stirpium Britannicarum* (Fascicule[7] of British Plants), as a slim volume of only 32 pages. Raven (1942 pp.244-7) gives full details of the *Fasciculus* including his intention to publish a Flora of Britain:

'Next spring if God give me strength and health I have decided to publish a **Synopsis stirpium Britannicarum** *(Flora of Britain), with brief and characteristic notes not only of the genera but of all particular species: it will not exceed the size of a Catalogue but will give the careful reader, even without pictures, a clear and unmistakable knowledge of each.'*

THE FLORA OF BRITAIN

The Flora was published in 1690 and was the culmination of all his previous work from the *Cambridge Catalogue* thirty years earlier to the first two volumes of the *Historia Plantarum*. He had been given a great deal of help by many correspondents from various parts of Britain who had collected and sent him material. They included James Bobart, curator of the Medical Garden at Oxford, Samuel Dale, his great friend from Braintree, James Petiver, Robert Plot the first curator of the Ashmolean Museum at Oxford (famous for his natural histories of Oxfordshire and Warwickshire) and his assistant Edward Lhwyd; Hans Sloane, and William Sherard, fellow of St John's College, Oxford. He acknowledges their help in the preface and also Tancred Robinson for proof reading and improving the script.

JOANNIS RAII

DE

Variis Plantarum Methodis

DISSERTATIO

BREVIS.

In qua agitur

I. De Methodi Origine & Progreſſu.
II. De Notis Generum characteriſticis.
III. De Methodo ſua in Specie.
IV. De Notis quas reprobat & rejicien-
das cenſet D. *Tournefort.*
V. De Methodo Tournefortiana.

LONDINI:

Impenſis *S. Smith* & *B. Walford,* Societatis
Regiæ Typographorum, ad Inſignia Principis in Cœmeterio D. Pauli. 1696.

Title-page of Ray's *Brief Dissertation.*

    Due to its great popularity and success as the first national
flora it sold out within four years, necessitating a second,
enlarged edition in 1696 containing many new species. It also
had an appendix on classification containing answers to
criticisms he had received from Rivinus and Tournefort. The high
esteem in which this edition was held is indicated by Smith[8]
writing in 1819:
    *'Of all the systematical and practical floras of any
country, the second edition of Ray's* **Synopsis** *is the most
perfect that ever came under our observation. He examined every
plant recorded in his work, and even gathered most of them
himself. He investigated their synonyms with consummate
accuracy; and if the clearness and precision of other authors
had equalled his, he would scarcely have committed an error.'*
    Raven, (1942 pp.258-9) summarized his achievement:
    *'It gave to any student of the country's plants a working
guide to identification, locality and habit...apart from the
Linnean nomenclature, we have a modern hand-book. The survey of
species is remarkably accurate, at least in the flowering
plants. The country has been adequately explored. The names and
brief descriptions make identification easy. The classification,
if not scientifically perfect, follows a natural sequence, and
is as easy to use as the modern scheme.* **British botany has been
given a secure and intelligible foundation.***'*
    The Flora was his last work on British botany and Ray would
have been delighted to have known that a third edition[9], edited
by Dillenius[10], was issued posthumously in 1724. This contained
twenty four plates of illustrations, (one of which is shown on
page 40), and continued as the standard guide, for use in the
field, for generations of students and botanists for over a
century after his death.

CATALOGUE OF EUROPEAN PLANTS
    In 1694 Ray published a revised version of the Catalogue of
Foreign Plants that had appeared at the back of his *Observations*
(p.31) under the title *Stirpium Europaearum extra Britannias
nascentium Sylloge*, with the dedication to Edward Bullock of
nearby Faulkbourne Hall. In Raven's view (1942 pp.283-5) the
chief importance of the *Sylloge* lies in the preface in which Ray
discusses various methods of classification and defends his
system against that of Rivinus (Bachmann), who based his method
on the shape of the flower. His answer to Rivinus was also
expanded two years later in the appendix to the second edition
of the Flora of Britain.

PLANTS OF EACH COUNTY in CAMDEN'S BRITANNIA
    In a letter to Lhwyd[11] dated June 1 1694 [i.e.1695], Ray
mentions that the publishers of Camden's *Britannia* had asked him
to contribute catalogues of plants for each county for a new
edition to be edited by Edmund Gibson. He in due course obliged,
though for Wales he referred them to Lhwyd and the details for
Middlesex were supplied by Petiver.
    The new edition was published in 1695 and in the preface Ray
was mentioned as *'the Great Botanist of our age.'* Raven, (1942,
pp.267-9), gives critical comment on each of the county lists
and mentions that *'though he had something to say at first-hand
about almost every county...the notes are generally too scrappy
to give any real idea of a county's plant-life.'* The lists were
useful however in that they stimulated the interests of others.

JOANNIS RAJI

Societatis Regiæ Socii,

METHODUS
PLANTARUM

EMENDATA ET AUCTA.

In quâ

Notæ maxime Characteristicæ exhibentur,
quibus Stirpium Genera tum summa,
tum infima cognoscuntur & à se mutuo
dignoscuntur,

Non necessariis omissis.

Accedit
METHODUS
GRAMINUM, JUNCORUM
ET
CYPERORUM
Specialis.

EODEM AUCTORE.

LONDINI,

Impensis *Samuelis Smith* & *Benjamini Walford* Typographorum Regiæ Societatis, ad insignia Principis
in Cœmeterio D. Pauli. MDCCIII.

Et veneunt
Amstelædami apud *Janssonio-Waasbergios,*

BRIEF DISSERTATION

In 1695 Ray received a copy of de Tournefort's *Elemens de Botanique* (1694) written in French. In it he condemned Ray's work and proposed a method of classification based on only one feature of the plant. As Tournefort was a leading French botanist, Ray felt that he should answer the criticisms and as Raven (1942, p.289) puts it, *'prevent systematic botany from receiving a fatal set-back.'*

As the second edition of the Flora of Britain was in hand, Ray managed to include a postscript of four pages giving a preliminary response. His full reply however was in his Brief Dissertation, a small treatise of just sixty four pages on the different methods of classifying plants; now one of Ray's least common works; which was published in 1696 with the title *Joannis Raii de Variis Plantarum Methodus Dissertatio Brevis*. (The title page is shown on page 42.) It was a continuation of his earlier discussions, and was mainly an answer to Tournefort.

THE METHODUS EMENDATA

Apart from the Volume III of his *Historia*, Ray's final work on botany was his *Methodus Plantarum Emendata et Aucta* (1703). (See title page opposite). He gave as his chief reason for writing it his awareness of some defects in the *Historia Plantarum*.

In it can be seen the culmination of his life's work on classification. He had begun in the Cambridge Catalogue with the four-fold divisions of Theophrastus: herbs, shrubs, under-shrubs and trees; in the *Methodus Nova* the undershrubs had been dropped; in the *Historia* the shrubs and trees were grouped together and in this last work he had only trees and shrubs. He reviewed all his previous work and that of others, made many improvements at all levels and specified six rules for those wishing to carry out classification. e.g. characters used should easily be seen by students without the aid of a microscope. Gunawardena (1933, pp.124-33) gives a particularly good summary of his achievements and his comment (p.9) is a fitting conclusion to Ray's work on plants:

'The *Methodus Emendata* is his greatest contribution to systematic botany. Creature of his time, he has created the model on which our own systems are based.'

NOTES TO CHAPTER 4

1. Lankester's *Correspondence* (1848), pp.139-40 and 160-1.
2. Sir Hans Sloane's collections founded the British Museum (Natural History). His herbarium is one of the major items in the Dept. of Botany and houses many of Ray's dried specimens. (Others are in the collections of the library of the University of Nottingham). Sloane's own annotated copy of Ray's *Historia Plantarum* is also there. (See Dandy, 1958).
3. See Mayr, (1982 pp.256-7).
4. See Letter to Dr Robinson, 1684. (*Correspondence* p.155).
5. An advertisement for this appears at the back of Ray's posthumous work, *Synopsis Methodica Avium - Piscium*, (1713). (See Keynes, 1951, p.79).
6. He advertised it at 'Price Four Pence'. Keynes, (1951, p.19).
7. A fascicule is part of a book published in instalments.
8. See Lankester, (1846), *Memorials of John Ray*, p.78.
9. Reproduced in facsimile by the Ray Society in 1973.
10. The first Sherardian Professor of Botany at Oxford.
11. See *Further Correspondence* p.244.

Plate from Willughby's *Ornithology* (1676).

CHAPTER 5

ZOOLOGY

'Ray - The father of modern systematic zoology.' Gregory[1].

INTRODUCTION

Great as were Ray's works in botany, his achievements in
zoology were perhaps even more remarkable and extensive, as they
were not his main interest and were fitted in between his
botanical studies. He wrote books on birds, fishes, mammals and
reptiles, and insects and in each of these subjects he laid the
foundations for future scientific progress.

He initially turned his attention to zoology, in order to
fulfill his obligations to his late friend and benefactor
Willughby. By this time he already had a trained scientific
mind, which was to enable him to bring order out of the chaos
that existed. He studied the previous zoological literature and
rejected all that was irrelevant or based on superstition and
astrology. He collated names and descriptions, established
natural criteria for species and higher taxonomic categories
based on significant structural features, and combined his own
great powers of observation with a genius for exact description
- later to be described by Gilbert White as unrivalled.

His classifications were entirely practical and were designed
to help beginners identify specimens. He emphasized the study of
the behaviour of the living animal, the importance of
recognizing differences solely due to sexual dimorphism and
seasonal colour changes e.g. the brown summer coat of the stoat
changing to white in the winter; and the need to consider all
stages of the life cycle, particularly of insects, in the
identification and naming of species. His first zoological work
which was on birds, was written in Latin and published in
Willughby's name in 1676 as the *Ornithologiae*.

WILLUGHBY'S ORNITHOLOGY

*'The foundations of scientific ornithology were laid by the
joint[2] labours of Francis Willughby and John Ray.'* Newton[3].

The objects and scope of the Ornithology are clearly laid out
in the preface: *'Our main design was to illustrate the History
of Birds, which is (as we said before of Animals in general) in
many particulars confused and obscure, by so accurately
describing each kind, and observing their Characteristic and
distinctive notes, that the reader might be sure of our meaning,
and upon comparing any Bird with our description not fail of
discerning whether it be the described or no...This then being
our design, we did not as some before us have done, only
transcribe other men's descriptions, but we ourselves did
carefully describe each bird from the view and inspection before
us.'*

In doing this, the mistakes of previous writers are
corrected, particularly relating to the many names and
descriptions in current use: *'...their mistakes are especially
in the multiplying of species, and making two or three sorts of
one.'* Though in the preface it is claimed that everything not
strictly relating to natural history is omitted, this is not
quite true as will be seen below.

The classification is a considerable advance on anything
previously used and clearly bears the stamp of Ray's authority
and his use of anatomy and the relation of form to function[4]:
'The whole Work we have divided into three Books. In the

Plate from Willughby's *Ornithology* (1676).

*first we treat of Birds in general; in the second of Land-fowl;
in the third of Water-Fowl. The second Book we have divided into
two parts: The first whereof contains Birds of crooked Beak and
Talons; the   second,   such   whose Bills and Claws are more
streight. The third book is tripartite: the first part takes in
all birds that wade in the waters, or frequent watery places,
but swim not; The second, such as are of a middle nature between
swimmers and waders, or rather that partake of both kinds, some
whereof are cloven-footed, and yet swim; others whole-footed,
but yet very long-leg'd like the waders: The third is of
whole-footed, or fin-toed Birds, that swim in the water.'*

   Raven (1942, p.325), as a very experienced ornithologist,
commented: *'He had based his system upon accurate study and
dissection; he had tried to take the whole life and structure of
each   species   into   account;   he has given us the first
'scientific' classification.'* The entries are mainly descriptive
covering plumage and structure, though occasionally some details
of habit and locality are given.

   Well-known fabulous Birds such as the Phoenixes, Griffins,
Harpyes and Ruk [= Roc], are specifically excluded, but where
there is doubt or suspicion, names and descriptions taken mainly
from Hernandez[5]; are included in an appendix, to ensure that
nothing is missed, and it is left to the readers to judge for
themselves the validity of the entry.

   Ray had a remarkable anatomical[6] knowledge of birds, having
carried out dissections from his early days at Cambridge and
particularly during his continental tour. As he had already
demonstrated with plants, he had an excellent eye for detail.
Describing the feet of the Bittern on page 282: *'The Toes great,
and very long , armed also with long and strong Talons; that of
the middle Toe serrated on the interiour edge, in like manner,
and for the same purpose, viz. of holding fast eels, and other
slippery fish, as in the rest of this kind.'* This is then
followed by a little snippet of non-ornithological data: *'The
back-claw, which is remarkable thick and long above the rest, is
wont to be set in Silver for a Pick-tooth, and is thought to
have a singular property of preserving the teeth.'*

   He was not averse to adding a lighter touch to his work and
in the section on Frugivorous Hook-bill'd Birds or Parrots on
page 109, his little story is so delicious it is quoted in full
as written: *'I shall not think much to set down one very
pleasant story, which Gesner said was told him by a certain
friend, of a Parrot, which fell out of King Henry VIII. his
Palace at Westminster into the River of Thames that runs by, and
then very seasonably remembring the words it had often heard,
some whether in danger or in jest, use, cried out amain, A Boat,
a Boat, for twenty pound. A certain experienced boatman made
thither presently, took up the bird, and restored it to the
King, to whom he knew it belonged, hoping for as great a reward
as the Bird had promised. The King agreed with the boatman that
he should have as the Bird being asked anew should say: And the
Bird answers, Give the Knave a Groat.'*

   In scientific terms the Ornithology achieved all it set out
to do and its appeal was greatly enhanced by the large number of
illustrated plates which were paid for by Mrs Willughby. The
drawings for these were gathered from sources throughout Europe
including many that had been collected by Willughby himself. The
engravings for the plates were produced in London and as Ray was
not able to supervise the work directly the results were not

50

Allegorical frontispiece from Willughby's *History of Fishes*.

always to his satisfaction, and though many are excellent there
is a considerable variation in quality. The Ornithology however
still contains the some of the finest illustrations of all Ray's
works and two plates have been selected as examples here. (See
pp.46 and 48).

Despite the illustrations and the overall magnificence of the
book, the use of Latin limited its appeal and Ray was asked to
produce an English[7] version. This appeared in 1678 with several
new sections on falconry, the care of small birds in cages and
wild-fowling, and was much more successful.

The ornithology inspired a whole sucession of later workers
including Linnaeus, Buffon, and Gilbert White. As one well-known
ornithologist commented (Raven, 1942, p.326): *'The book itself
will always remain an object of reverence to the ornithologist
and of admiration to the historian. When we consider the
confusion of its predecessors, the short time and scanty
material available to its authors, and the difficulties of the
subject in days when collecting and observation had none of
their modern instruments, the quality of the achievement stands
out.'*

THE HISTORY OF FISHES

Ray's earliest published work on fishes were the Table of
Fishes he helped Willughby with for Wilkins's *Real Character*[8]
and two appendices he produced for his *Collection of English
Words* in 1673, which were catalogues of *Fish from near Penzance
and St Ives*, and of *Freshwater Fish found in England*; the
material for these having been derived from observations made on
his travels.

After finishing the Ornithology Ray immediately began work on
the History of Fishes in continuation of his obligation to
Willughby. He followed a similar method in that he carefully
examined all the previous authorities; a much more arduous task
than with the birds, as there were a far greater number of books
to contend with. The main sources he used were Rondelet's *De
Piscibus Marinis*, published at Lyons in 1554 and Salviani's
Aquatilium Animalium Historiae published at Rome, also in 1554.
Many of the best plates that Ray used originated from Salviani,
and he certainly consulted the works of Gesner, Belon, Aldrovani
and many others.

Unfortunately, due to the remarriage of Mrs Willughby, she
lost interest in Ray's work connected with her first husband,
and Ray had to leave Middleton Hall during his work on the
fishes. This added considerably to his problems as he no longer
had access to Willughby's collections or notes. Nevertheless
with the help of his many friends and his own prodigious
energies he completed the work and, with it, his obligation to
Willughby. With no funds forthcoming from Willughby's widow for
plates, the manuscript lay in a dusty drawer[9] until his friend
Dr Tancred Robinson drew the attention of the Royal Society to
it in 1685. The Society agreed to publish it and the president
himself, Samuel Pepys,[10] contributed fifty pounds which was used
to pay for seventy nine plates. His example was followed by many
others, though to a lesser extent, and included many famous
scientists of the day such as Christopher Wren, Robert Boyle,
John Evelyn and Elias Ashmole, the names of the contributors
appearing at the bottom of each plate they paid for.

The *Historia Piscium* was published in 1686,[11] the same year
as the first volume of the *Historia Plantarum*, and was a

Synopfis Methodica

Animalium Quadrupedum

E T

Serpentini Generis.

Vulgarium Notas Charaĉteriſticas,
Rariorum Defcriptiones integras exhibens:
cum Hiſtoriis & Obſervationibus Anato-
micis perquam curioſis.

*Præmittuntur nonnulla De Animalium in
genere, Senſu, Generatione, Diviſione,* &c.

Auĉtore *JOANNE RAIO,* S. R. S.

Imprimatur,

15 *Junt,*   *Robert Southwell,* R.S.P.
1693.

L O N D I N I:
Impenſis *S. Smith* & *B. Walford* Societatis
Regiæ Typographorum ad Inſignia Prin-
cipis in Cœmeterio D. Pauli. 1693.

Title-page of Ray's *Synopsis of Animals and Reptiles.* (1693)

magnificent folio production in which many of the 187 plates of
illustrations were of a very high quality. The most accurate
were those engraved from recent drawings of fresh specimens,
while those copied from earlier works were generally of a much
lower standard. The allegorical frontispiece or preliminary
title page is quite the most superb illustration in any of Ray's
works and is a splendid example of the craft of the engraver at
its peak. It is reproduced here on page 50, though, at a quarter
the size of the original, it is not seen to full advantage.
　　The main text comprises four books. The first has general
information covering the definition of a fish, several chapters
on anatomical details including a long discourse on the function
of the air-bladder, reproduction, food, age, growth and
classification. He ends with a list of British fish grouped
within the new classification, whilst the remaining three books
deal with the detailed descriptions.
　　An extract from Raven's (1942, p.365) translation of the
Epilogue gives Ray's thoughts on his own work: *'We
have..attempted..only to record the observations of ourselves or
our friends or of reliable authorities. We shrink from
unnecessary multiplication of species, and to avoid it have
visited almost all the chief fishing ports of England, and the
markets of Belgium, Germany, Italy, and France; have bought all
the species new to us and described them so that the reader can
easily recognise them. we cannot claim to have found many new
species; we have found some and can claim to have described,
discriminated and classified more accurately.'*

THE SYNOPSIS OF ANIMALS AND REPTILES
*'One of the great landmarks in the history of Vertebrate
Zoology.'* Gregory[1]
　　In a letter to Ray written in Geneva in April 1684, his great
friend Dr Tancred Robinson expressed his delight that Ray was
compiling a general history of plants and continued: *'I am in
great hopes that you will bestow on the world a general history
of nature; it is very defective at present, and seems to call
for method and perfection from you.'* The idea was for Ray to
produce a series of synopses or hand-books on plants, animals
and fossils. The plants have been covered earlier and as part of
the overall plan for the animals Ray published a Synopsis of
Animals [= mammals] and Reptiles in 1693 with the title *Synopsis
Methodica Animalium Quadrupedum et Serpentini Generis*.
　　Despite his considerable experience in dissection[12] from his
Cambridge days and in particular from his stay in Italy, and his
knowledge of physiology from reading, this was relatively new
ground for Ray. By now however he knew what to look for in the
literature and this, coupled with his incomparable knowledge of
the principles of classification, enabled him to produce yet
another scientific masterpiece. The value of his contribution on
mammals was summed up nearly ninety years later by Thomas
Pennant:[13] *'...in living at a period when the study of Natural
History was just beginning to dawn in these Kingdoms, he was
obliged to content himself with giving descriptions of the few
animals brought over here and collecting the rest of his
material from other writers. Yet so correct was his genius that
we see a systematic arrangement arising even from the chaos of
Aldrovandi and Gesner. Under his hand the indigested matter of
those able and copious writers assumes a new form, and the whole
is made clear and perspicuous.'*

60   *De Animalibus in genere.*

Animalium Viviparorum Quadrupedum Tabula.

Animalia Vivipara pilosa seu Quadrupeda sunt, vel
┌ *Ungulata,* eáque vel
│ ┌ Μονόγυλα, i. e. *Solidipeda,* Equus, Asinus, Zebra.
│ │ Δίγυλα, i. e. *Bisulca,* seu ungulâ bifidâ, quæ vel
│ │ ┌ *Ruminantia,*Μηρυκίζοντα,*cornibus* ┌ 1. *Bovinum.*
│ │ │ ┌ *Perpetuis ,* quorum tria sunt
│ ┤ ┤ ┤ genera ┤ 2. *Ovinum.*
│ │ │ └ *Deciduis, Cervinum* genus. └ 3. *Caprinum.*
│ │ └ *Non ruminantia,* Genus *Porcinum.*
│ └ Τετράγυλα seu *Quadrisulca,* Rhinoceros, Hippopo-
│   tamus, *&c.*
└ *Unguiculata,* quæ pede sunt vel
   ┌ *Bifido,* duobus duntaxat unguibus donato, *Ca-*
   ┤ *melinum* genus.
   └ *Multifido,* πολυσχιδῆ, quæ vel sunt
     ┌ *Digitis indivisis,*sibi invicem cohærentibus &
     │ communi cute tectis, eorum tantùm extre-
     │ mis in margine pedis extantibus, & ungui-
     ┤ bus obtusis munitis ; *Elephas.*
     │ *Digitis aliquousque separatis* & à se invicem
     └ divisis, quæ vel
       ┌ Πλατυώνυχα & 'Ανθρωπόμορφα, *Simiæ.*
       ┤ *Unguibus angustioribus,*Dentibus primoribus
       └ seu incisoribus in utraque maxilla, vel
         ┌ *Pluribus,*Hæc autem omnia vel carnivora
         │ & rapacia sunt,vel saltem insectivora,
         │ aut victu promiscuo ex Insectis &
         │ Vegetabilibus.
         │ ┌ *Majora,* rostro
         ┤ │ ┌ *Brevi,* capite rotundiore *Felinum* genus.
         │ │ └ *Productiore,* Genus *Caninum.*
         │ │ *Minora,* corpore longo gracili, cruri-
         │ │ bus brevibus *Vermineum* genus, seu
         │ └ *Mustelinum.*
         │ *Binis insignioribus,* cujus generis species
         └ omnes phytivoræ sunt, *Leporinum* genus.

E

Table from Ray's *Synopsis of Animals and Reptiles* showing the classification of quadrupeds.

It is fortunate that much of Ray's voluminous correspondence
has not only survived, but has also been published. A study of
the letters to and from Ray sheds much light on both Ray and his
times. As an example, a letter[14] of August 24, 1692 written in
connection with the Synopsis of Animals, contains an item of
local ornithological interest: *'They tell of Eagles about
Tiptree heath that come over in summer time & sometimes have
bred thereabouts.'* In Ray's time the post office did not exist,
houses were not identified, carriers did much of the work of
transporting letters, and accommodation addresses were often
used. The one at the head of Ray's letter just mentioned was
addressed: For Mr.JOHN AUBREY[15] at the Tobacco-roll & Sugar loaf
at the upper end of Mayden-head-lane opposite the gap in great
Russell street/London.

The *Synopsis* starts with introductory essays on animals in
general. In these he deals with questions such as "What is an
animal?" He discusses conscious awareness, intelligence and
various philosophical arguments. He specifically rejects the
theory of the spontaneous generation of animals and looks at the
problems of deciding whether animals were all created in the
beginning, (i.e. whether the 'eggs' of all future generations
were present in the first animals), or are produced individually
at each generation. As a part of this last process, the recent
discovery by Leeuwenhoek of spermatozoa, had raised a further
problem which Ray outlined, of deciding whether individuals
originated in the ovum of the female or in the sperm of the
male. (Raven, 1942,p.377).

The major part however of the essays, and the format on which
he based the rest of the book, is his classification. In this
Ray followed the Aristotelian method of dichotomous analysis in
which everything is divided on the basis of falling into one of
only two categories. His first main division is *Sanguinea* and
Exanguia, roughly corresponding to vertebrates and
invertebrates. The former are divided by their of method of
respiration into those with *lungs* and those with *gills*. The
air-breathers are split on the basis of the number of ventricles
in the heart: quadrupeds, cetaceans and birds with two; and
amphibians, lizards and snakes with only one.

The quadrupeds are further separated in considerable detail
and Gregory (1910 p.22) provides an excellent example of the
dichotomous method applied at eight further levels to separate
cats and dogs. They are given in order of importance: (1) number
of feet (*quadrupeda*); (2) hoofed or *clawed*; (3) bifid or
multifid; (4) with digits unseparated or *separated* ; (5) flat
clawed or *narrow clawed* and with incisors in each jaw; (6)
incisors *several, habits carnivorous, insectivorous* or
omnivorous, or (7) *larger* or smaller forms; (8)
head *rounder* (Cats) or *longer* (Dogs).

Despite the inherent defects of a dichotomous system as
viewed today, at the time it represented a tremendous advance
and formed the scientific foundations for future systematic
zoology. Gregory, (1910, p.22), comments: *'Ray may be justly be
regarded as the founder of modern zoology. He was the great
figure of the seventeenth century, as was Linnaeus of the
eighteenth and Cuvier of the early nineteenth. More logical and
analytical, while perhaps less original and synthetic in his
genius than Linnaeus, he indeed made a pathway in the zoological
field which Linne was glad to follow, and to some extent he
anticipated the brightest thoughts of the great Swede.'*

E Bibl. Linn. 1784. JESmith

HISTORIA
INSECTORUM.

Autore *JOANNE RAIO*,

Collegii S. Trinitatis apud Cantabrigienfes, &
Societatis Regiæ olim Socio.

OPUS POSTHUMUM

Juffu Regiæ Societatis Londinenfis
Editum.

Cui fubjungitur Appendix de *Scarabæis Britannicis*,
Autore *M. LISTER* S. R. S. ex MSS. Mufæi
Afhmolæani.

LONDINI:

Impenfis A. & J. Churchill, ad infigne Nigri Cycni
in vico dicto *Pater-nofter-row*. M.DCC.X.

INSECTS

It was natural that Ray should have been interested in insects from the beginning. As a keen observer of all natural history, his early work in botany would inevitably have brought him into contact with many different kinds of insect, who were equally interested in plants but for somewhat different reasons. His Cambridge Catalogue is full of notes and observations e.g. on Sopewort [=Soapwort (*Saponaria officinalis* L)] from Ewen & Prime, (1975, p.111): *'One of the papilio media (butterflies) of Moufet (Theat.insect.* p.105) *delights to sit on this plant in the month of August; it is notable not only for its very swift flight but also for its very long proboscis and the loud noise which it emits, almost like that of a hornet.'*

During his collecting and travelling days he had left the insects to Willughby and due to his other commitments he was unable to start work on them until 1690. It was also unfortunate that he was only able to gain access to Willughby's notes in 1704, a year before he died. Compared with other areas of biology the literature was particularly sparce, the two main sources being Moffet's[16] *Insectorum Theatrum* (Theatre of Insects), (1634); and Swammerdam's History of Insects, (1669).

In his last years, due to his infirmity, Ray was far more dependent upon others to provide materials for his History of Insects. He relied for some of his specimens on friends and correspondents including the Bobarts at Oxford, Samuel Dale, the Braintree doctor, and James Petiver. The majority of his specimens however were obtained by his wife and three daughters who all collected caterpillars, moths, butterflies and other insects within a radius of two to three miles of their house.

Ray was persuaded by his friends to produce a preliminary classification and this was published in 1705 as a small booklet of only 10 pages with the title *Methodus Insectorum*. Unfortunately the immense labour of sorting, describing and classifying the large number of insects found, was beyond him, and the main work, his *Historia Insectorum,* was unfinished at his death. Even so he had left adequate notes for an editor, but when the work was published in 1710 it was much as he had left it, as no one had been found willing or able to undertake the task.

Despite this drawback the *Historia Insectorum* contained details of many new species, the foundation of a classification and a considerable amount of data on many groups including butterflies, moths, beetles, wasps, flies, bugs, fleas, ticks, worms, leeches, spiders, millipedes, dragonflies, bees and grasshoppers. One of its major advances was due to Ray's appreciation of the need to describe the life histories of insects, including every stage of the metamorphosis of each species. (Lisney, 1960, p.27).

There can be no more fitting conclusion to this section than to quote Raven's translation (p.407) from the History of Insects, of what must be one of the most beautiful pieces of natural history prose ever written:

'You ask what is the use of butterflies? I reply to adorn the world and delight the eyes of men: to brighten the countryside like so many golden jewels. To contemplate their exquisite beauty and variety is to experience the truest pleasure. To gaze enquiringly at such elegance of colour and form designed by the ingenuity of nature and painted by her artist's pencil, is to acknowledge and adore the imprint of the art of God.'

Joannis Raii

SYNOPSIS

METHODICA

Avium & Piscium;

OPUS POSTHUMUM,

QUOD

Vivus recensuit & perfecit ipse
insignissimus Author :

IN QUO

Multas SPECIES, in ipsius Ornitho-
logiâ & Ichthyologia desideratas, adjecit :
Methodumque suam PISCIUM Naturæ
magìs convenientem reddidit.

CUM

Appendice, & Iconibus.

LONDINI:

Impensis GULIELMI INNYS, ad Insignia Principis in Cœmeterio D. *Pauli.*
MDCCXIII.

SYNOPSIS OF BIRDS AND FISHES

Even before the Synopsis of Animals was finished, Ray had started work on its sequel, the *Synopsis Methodica Avium et Piscium*, which he completed in record time, as in a letter to Lhwyd[17] dated 10th June 1694, he reported that it had been at the printers for some while. Due to the death of the printer and other problems it was not published till 19 years later in 1713.

Though the title page, opposite, indicates that it was one book, it was actually two completely separate books bound in together, each with their own sub-title pages and pagination. Both books were basically summaries of the works he wrote in Willughby's name, with additions. He produced concise descriptions of each species, of such excellence, that they enabled identifications to be made quickly and simply, and it was used by many generations of students.

It had a considerable influence on later workers including Linnaeus, Buffon and our own Gilbert White and as Raven (1942, p.369) points out, it was White's starting point and his text-book. Of the *Synopses* in general, Raven's words cannot be bettered:

'The debt which natural history in Britain, and indeed the world over, owes to them can hardly be overstated.'

NOTES TO CHAPTER 5

1. *The Orders of Mammals*, (1910), p.16
2. Up until the formation of the Ray Society in 1844 most of Willughby's *Ornithology* had been attributed to Willughby and little to Ray. Subsequent opinion has reversed this thinking and full details of the evidence are given in Raven, (1942) chapter 12.
3. *A Dictionary of Birds*, (1893-96), p.7.
4. Raven, (1942), p.323.
5. *Plantas y Animales de la Nueva Espana*, Mexico, 1615.
6. His knowledge was matched by that of his biographer Charles Raven, who as an ornithologist, was held in particularly high esteem in Russia. During a dinner there he identified correctly, from a single bone, the species of a quite unusual bird featuring in the main course. See Dillistone, (1975).
7. The English version (folio) was reproduced in facsimile in 1972.
8. See p.27.
9. The exact length of time it lay there is unknown but it was probably at least two years as he would have finished it before starting writing the *Historia Plantarum* in 1683.
10. The well-known diarist.
11. The date of 1685 on the frontispiece is the date of authorization by the Royal Society of funds for the production of the book, and is not the publication date.
12. Ray dissected a porpoise in 1669 and published a detailed account of it in the *Philosophical Transactions* of the Royal Society. See *Further Correspondence*, pp.58-62.
13. *History of Quadrupeds*, (1781). See Gregory, (1910), p.17.
14. *Further Correspondence*, pp.174-7.
15. Antiquary, Fellow of the Royal Society and one-time tutor to the family of Edward Bullock of Faulkbourne Hall in Essex.
16. His daughter may have been the little Miss Muffet of nursery rhyme fame. See Lisney, (1960), p.5.
17. *Further Correspondence*, p.249.

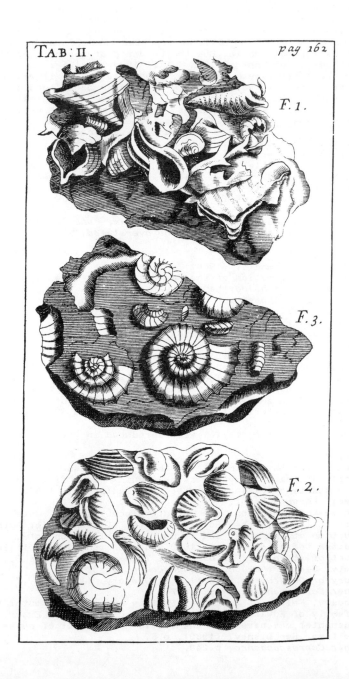

TAB: II.   pag 162

F. 1.

F. 3.

F. 2.

CHAPTER 6

GEOLOGY AND FOSSILS

INTRODUCTION

In his work on geology and palaeontology Ray was one of the earliest pioneers. In his many writings on the subject, both in his letters and published works, he clearly showed an amazing grasp of the subject.

During his continental tour he had spent some time with Nicolaus Steno whose *De Solido intra Solidum naturaliter contento* (1669), more succinctly known as the *Prodromus*, is generally regarded as the starting point of modern scientific geological studies. Ray would therefore have been familiar with his views at first hand and he certainly read the *Prodromus* on publication.

Some of Ray's earliest and finest geological work can be found in his *Observations* of 1673, though his major book in this branch of science was the *Miscellaneous Discourses* first published in 1692. In addition, the preface to the second edition of his Flora of Britain of 1696, contains an apology for omitting a good number of the plants which formerly existed in this island, and he also discusses the problems of reconciling an organic origin of these fossils with the biblical account of the deluge. (Raven, 1942, pp.255-6).

OBSERVATIONS

In the *Observations* (see page 73), he devotes a 19 page essay to fossils, giving a detailed account of those seen in England and on the continent, and in so doing provides what must be the very first directory of fossiliferous localities:

*'And first I shall make a particular enumeration of some of the most remarkable places where they have been found, as well as in **England** as beyond the Seas, partly out of my own Observation, partly out of good Writers. Secondly, I shall give the opinions of the best Authors concerning the Origin and Production of them.'* A long list of place names then follows e.g.: *'**Whitby**: Besides Serpent-Stones* [= Ammonites], *we found there both upon the Shores and in the rocky Cliffs by the sea-side petrified muscles and **Belemnites** in great plenty. **Kinesham** [Keynsham[1]]: Of these Serpent-Stones we saw several sorts here, and some of that extraordinary bigness that (as I remember) they were about a Foot in diameter. **Farnham** in Surrey, **Richmond** in Yorkshire, **Lyme** in Dorset...'* He continues (p.115):

*'Besides these petrified Shells there are found in several places of **England** other congenerous Bodies, viz. **Star stones**, by some called **Astroites** [=* Asterozoa or starfish]. (2.) *S. Cuthbert's beads or **Trochites** [=* Stem or arm ossicles from sea-lilies] *and (3.) Cap-Stones or **Echinites**, called by Naturalists **Lapides brontiae** [=* Sea-urchins].' For the Glossopetrae [= Sharks teeth], localities are given in Belgium, Germany and later in Malta; and many other places throughout Europe are mentioned together with the specimens found there.

In discussing their origin (p.120) he gives an advanced view for his times: *'The first and most probable Opinion is that they were originally the Shells or Bones of living Fishes and other Animals bred in the Sea. This was the general Opinion of the Ancients, insomuch as **Steno** saith.'* He goes on to discuss their mode of preservation in excellent detail, and in describing the details of ammonites he provides an account that would grace a modern text-book, both in style and accuracy: (p.122).

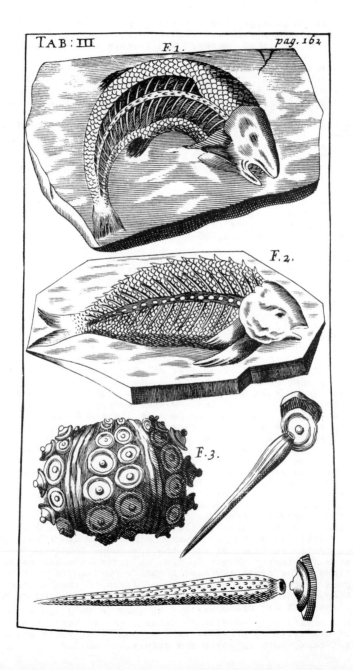

TAB: III   F.1.   pag. 162

F.2.

F.3.

*'They likewise some of them retained all along the surface of them very pretty kind of Sutures, such as are observed in the Skulls of several kinds of living Creatures, which Sutures were most curiously shaped in the manner of Leaves and every one of them in the same Shell exactly like one another... All these Sutures I found by breaking some of the Stones to be the **Termini** or bounding of certain **Diaphragms** or partitions, which seemed to divide the Cavity of the Shell into a multitude of very proportionate and regular Cells or Caverns...'*

Two of the major problems facing early geologists were (1) the short length of time[2] available, since the creation, for geological processes to have taken place, and (2) a general disbelief in the extinction of species, as theology postulated that all creatures had been created in the beginning and were all still alive. Ray, unlike most of his contemporaries, was prepared to address both of these problems when the evidence and his observations conflicted with these beliefs:

On page 126 for example: *'In general since the most ancient times recorded in History, the face of the Earth has suffered little change,... whence it will follow, that if the Mountains were not from the beginning, either the World is a great deal older than is imagined or believed...or that in the primitive times and soon after the Creation the earth suffered far more concussions and mutations in its superficial part than afterwards.'* He continues:

'Among these petrified Shells are many sorts, which are not at this day that we know of any where to be found...If it be said, that these Species be lost out of the World: that is a supposition which Philosophers hitherto have been unwilling to admit.' Even if they accept that a few species may have been lost, the evidence shows that many species have gone and indeed whole genera: *'Such for example the **Serpentine** Stones or **Cornua Ammonis**, I myself have seen five or six distinct species, and doubtless there are many more.'* (How right he was!)

A well-reasoned account is also given of the probable methods of fossilization, followed by a powerful argument against fossils being distributed by the biblical deluge (p.125): *'First it will hence follow that all the Earth was once covered by the Sea, and that for a considerable time: for there being found of these Shells in the middle of Germany, at least 200 miles distant from any Sea, as myself can witness, nay, upon the highest Mountains of Europe, even the **Alps** themselves, the Sea must needs have covered them, and consequently, the water keeping its level, all **Europe** and the World besides. Now that ever the Water should have covered the Earth to that highth as to exceed the tops of the highest Mountains, and for a considerable time abode there, is hard to believe, nor can such an Opinion be easily reconciled with the Scriptures. If it be said that these Shells were brought in by the universal deluge in the time of **Noah**, when the Mountains were covered. I answer, that that Deluge proceeded from Rain, which was more likely to carry Shells down to the Sea, than bring any up from it.'*

In similar vein he attacks the theory of fossil formation due to a plastic power in the earth, using his own observations to back his superb logic. **Ray's essay in the *Observations* is a most remarkable contribution to geological science, in which he is far in advance of both his contemporaries and his times, and once again he shows an extraordinary flair for mastering the essentials of his subject.**

Three *Physico-Theological* DISCOURSES,

CONCERNING

I The Primitive C H A O S, and Creation of the World.

II. The General D E L U G E, its Causes and Effects.

III. The Dissolution of the W O R L D, and Future Conflagration.

WHEREIN

Are largely Discussed the Production and Use of Mountains ; the Original of Fountains, of Formed Stones, and Sea-Fishes Bones and Shells found in the Earth ; the Effects of particular Floods and Inundations of the Sea ; the Eruptions of *Vulcano's* ; the Nature and Causes of Earthquakes :

With an Historical Account of those Two late Remarkable Ones in *Jamaica* and *England*.
With P R A C T I C A L I N F E R E N C E S.

By *J O H N R A Y*, Fellow of the *Royal Society*

The *Second Edition* Corrected, very much Enlarged, and Illustrated with Copper-plates.

LONDON: Printed for *Sam. Smith*, at the *Princes Arms* in St. *Paul's* Church-yard. 1 6 9 3.

1818.

125.

MISCELLANEOUS DISCOURSES

In a letter[3] dated November 25th 1691 to Lhwyd[4] at Oxford, Ray wrote: *'The Discourse concerning the Dissolution of the World is finished & under the Presse. The Body or Skeleton of it is a sermon I preached above 30 years ago at S. Maries church in Cambridge upon 2 Pet. 3. 11.'* He describes the headings and some of the topics to be discussed e.g. The possibility of: (1) The waters returning again to cover the earth. (2) The extinction of the sun. (3) The erruption of the central fire. (4) A deflagration in the torrid Zone, and continues: *'Besides, there are two large Digressions, one concerning the general Deluge in the days of Noah: another concerning the primitive chaos & creation of the World. In the former of those at the instance & importunity of some friends I have inserted something concerning formed stones* [fossils] *as an effect of the deluge, I mean their Dispersion all over the Earth. Therefore you will find all I have to say in opposition to their opinion, who hold them to be primitive productions of Nature in imitation of shels...no man who hath written heertofore concerning the Deluge hath made any mention of them; & therefore such an addition, for the novelty of the matter would be acceptable to the curious, & give my book advantage of sale.'*

It was published in 1692 with the title *Miscellaneous Discourses concerning the Dissolution and Changes of the World*. It was written in English, had a ready sale and sold out quickly, necessitating a second edition the next year. To this Ray added considerably more material, increasing the number of pages from 285 to 438, rearranging it and producing what was almost a new book. The title was altered to *Three Physico-Theological Discourses* with the discourse titles and contents given as shown opposite. Four plates were added, one on ancient coins and three on fossils, two of which feature on pages 60 and 62. Subsequent editions appeared in 1713, 1721 and 1732.

The section on fossils starts with a statement of the current problem: (p.104). *'It is not yet agreed among the Learned whether these formed Stones be original Productions of Nature, formed in imitation of the Shells of Fishes; or the real Shells themselves...'* The arguments for both sides are then given; and one, in favour of an organic origin (pp.110-1), is quoted here: *'Nature makes nothing in vain. But these Teeth, were they just formed in the Earth, would be in vain; for they could not have any use of teeth... Nature never made teeth without a Jaw, nor Shells without an Animal Inhabitant, nor single Bones, no not in their own proper element, much less in a strange one.'*

Ray, who has largely been ignored by the historians of geology, can now be justly regarded as one of the founders of British geological science.

NOTES TO CHAPTER 6

1. Still a famous collecting area. During a bypass construction about 25 years ago, an estimated 10,000 ammonites were excavated, with many over two feet [0.61m] in diameter.
2. Popular estimates of the date of the formation of the earth varied from 4004 BC [at 3 o'clock in the afternoon (sic)] given by Archbishop Ussher, to some 5,600 years ago.)
3. *Further Correspondence*, pp.222-3.
4. Lhwyd, was one of the first British workers on fossils. See R.T. Gunther, 1945, Early Science in Oxford, **14**: *Life and Letters of Edward Lhwyd*.

A

COLLECTION

OF

Englifh PROVERBS

Digefted into a convenient Method for the
fpeedy finding any one upon occa-
fion; with

Short ANNOTATIONS.

Whereunto are added *Local Proverbs* with
their Explications, *Old Proverbial Rhythmes*
Lefs known or *Exotick Proverbial* **sentences**
and *Scottifh Proverbs.*

By *J. R.* M. A. and Fellow of the
Royal Society.

CAMBRIDGE,
Printed by *John Hayes,* Printer to the Univer-
fity, for *W. Morden.* 1670.

Joannes Rajus

Title-Page of the first edition of Ray's *English Proverbs* with
an added frontispiece, from his *Synopsis of Animals and Reptiles.*

CHAPTER 7

PROVERBS, ENGLISH WORDS AND THE LITTLE DICTIONARY

COLLECTION OF ENGLISH PROVERBS

Though Ray's name will forever be associated with natural history, it is characteristic of his wide range of interests and his versatility, that he should have made important contributions in an entirely different sphere.

During his British travels he collected not only biological specimens but also proverbs, unusual words and details of dialects and industrial processes. These were later published in book form, and the first, *A Collection of English Proverbs,* was issued in 1670, with a title page as shown opposite.

In the preface he defines a proverb as *'A Short Sentence or Phrase in common use containing some Trope, Figure, Homonymy, Rhythme or other novity of expression.'* he then continues: *'It's now some ten years or more since I began this Collection,...I read over all former printed Catalogues that I could meet with; then I observed all that occurred in familiar discourse, and employed my friends and acquaintances in several parts of England in the like observation and enquiry, who afforded me large contributions.'* (More or less the same method as used in his Catalogue of English Plants published the same year.) He lists the major reference works he consulted, including *The Children's Dictionary,* Camden's *Remains,* and Howell's *Paroemiographia.*

It is characteristic of his scientific training, that one of his first thoughts was how to classify them: *'When I thought I had a sufficient stock, I began to consider of a convenient Method to dispose them in, so as readily and easily to find any proverb upon occasion, for that I had observed wanting in all former Collections.'*

In his classification he uses a number of different headings, with an alphabetical arrangement within each. e.g:

SENTENCES AND PHRASES, MOST NOT NOW IN COMMON USE.
An Ape is an Ape, a varlet's a varlet
Though they be clad in silk or scarlet.
What *children* hear at home doth soon fly abroad.
A true *friend* should be like a privy – open in necessity.
PROVERBS BELONGING TO HEALTH, DIET AND PHYSICK.
After dinner sit a while, after supper walk a mile.
The best physicians are Dr Diet, Dr Quiet and Dr Merryman.
PROVERBS ON HUSBANDRY, WEATHER AND THE SEASONS OF THE YEAR.
March wind and May sun, make clothes white and maids dun.
When the wind's in the East,
It's neither good for man nor beast.
PROVERBS REFERRING TO LOVE, WEDLOCK AND WOMEN.
Marry your Sons when you will, your Daughters when you can.
A woman's mind and winter-wind change oft.
(He includes one rather immodest one in this section. In the second edition he apologises, but justifies its retention.)
PROVERBS THAT ARE ENTIRE SENTENCES.
Agree for the Law is costly.
Children and fools speak truth.
Little strokes fell great oaks.
Tidings *make either glad or sad.*
PROVERBS THAT ARE NOT ENTIRE SENTENCES.
To take *hair* of the same dog.
He *farts* frankincence. (An ancient Greek Proverb: Self-love makes even a man's vices and imperfections please him.)

A
COLLECTION
OF

English Words

N O T

GENERALLY USED.

W I T H

Their Significations and Original, in
two ALPHABETICAL CATALOGUES.

T H E O N E

Of fuch as are proper to the Northern, the
other to the Southern COUNTIES.

W I T H

An Account of the preparing and refining fuch
METALS and MINERALS as are found in
ENGLAND.

The FOURTH EDITION.
Augmented with many Hundred Words, Ob-
SERVATIONS, LETTERS, &c.

By JOHN RAY, F. R. S.

L O N D O N:

Printed for W. Otridge, oppofite the North Side of the New
Church in the Strand ; S. Bladon, in Pater-nofter-row ; W.
Cooke, at the Royal Exchange ; W. Harris, in St. Paul's
Church-Yard ; S. Steare and T. Peat, in Fleet-ftreet ; J.
Robfon, C. Parker, and W. Shropfhire, in Bond-ftreet; J.
Ridley, in St. James's-ftreet ; H. Turpin, in St. John's-
ftreet ; R. Smith, next Barnard's Inn, in Holborn ; G. Wood-
fall, at Charing-Crofs ; and G. Peach, Cheapfide.
MDCCLXVIII.

PROVERBIAL SIMILIES.
 As seasonable as snow in summer.
 As much wit as three folks - two fools and a mad man.
PROVERBIAL RHYTHMES AND OLD SAWS.
 The higher the plum-tree, the riper the plum,
 The richer the cobler, the blacker his thumb.
 A man of words and not of deeds,
 Is like a garden full of weeds.
DRINKING PHRASES.
 The difference between the poor man and the rich is,
 that the poor walketh to get meat for his stomack,
 the rich a stomack for his meat.
OUT OF DOCTOUR FULLERS WORTHIES OF ENGLAND.
 Cornwall: By Tre, Pol, and Pen,
             You shall know the Cornish men.
 Essex: Braintree for the pure, and Bocking for the poor,
             Cogshall for the jeering Town, and Kelvedon   for
             the whore.
SCOTTISH PROVERBS
 A friend is not known but in need.
 The book was immediately popular and his friends liked it so
much they sent in several hundred additions over the next few
years. These were incorporated into a second edition in 1678.
Further editions followed, up to a fifth in 1813, with re-issues
until 1855.
 For many of the proverbs, Ray is the earliest authority. His
many notes on meanings and origins are of great historical
interest, and for students of folklore and dialect, his work is
still of great value today. (Raven, 1942, p.168).

COLLECTION OF ENGLISH WORDS (1673).
 By 1673, Ray's lists of unusual words were not very long, and
to increase the size of his book, he added catalogues of English
Birds and Fishes and details of mining and industrial processes.
(The latter included the manufacture of vitriol in Essex).
 It's significance is summarised by Raven: (1942, p.169).
'...the first serious attempt to gather and preserve the
folk-speech and to distinguish the local dialects of England.'
 A greatly-enlarged second edition appeared in 1691. Two
subsequent editions were incorporated with English Proverbs and
the title-page of the fourth is shown opposite. Skeat's edition
of 1874 gives Ray high praise and called him 'the remote
ancestor of the English Dialect Society.' (Raven, 1942, p.171).

THE LITTLE DICTIONARY (1675).
 Ray's Dictionariolum Trilingue (Little three-language
dictionary) was first published in 1675, in English, Latin and
Greek. In his biological work he had found many errors in the
names in the literature. His first priority was to correct
these, and the main part of the Dictionary was concerned with
birds, plants and animals. He did not stop here however and
included stars, stones and metals, elements and meteors, parts
of the human body, food, diseases and clothing.
 Its practical utility was appreciated by many generations of
school children, and it ran into eight editions by 1736. The
title was changed to Nomenclator Classicus with the second
edition. It was reproduced in facsimile by the Ray Society in
1981, and still contains much of interest to a wide range of
natural and other historians.

THE

𝕎𝕚𝕤𝕕𝕠𝕞 𝕠𝕗 𝔾𝕠𝕕

Manifeſted in the

WORKS

OF THE

CREATION,

In Two Parts.

V I Z.

The Heavenly Bodies, Elements, Meteors,
Foſſils, Vegetables, Animals, (Beaſts, Birds,
Fiſhes, and Inſects) more particularly in the
Body of the Earth, its Figure, Motion, and
Conſiſtency, and in the admirable Structure
of the Bodies of Man, and other Animals,
as alſo in their Generation, *&c.*

By *J O H N R A Y*,
Fellow of the *Royal Society*.

The Second Edition, very much enlarged.

L O N D O N:
Printed for *Samuel Smith*, at the *Princes Arms*
in St. *Paul*'s Church-yard. 1 6 9 2.

CHAPTER 8

THE WISDOM OF GOD

How manifold are thy Works, O Lord?
In Wisdom hast thou made them all.[1]

Most of Ray's books had been involved with bringing order out of chaos. This he had done by observing, identifying, describing, defining and classifying his findings. The *Wisdom of God*, first published in 1691, differed significantly in its approach, as it was mainly concerned with interpretations of, and inductions from, these findings. The range of its scope is breathtaking, as he covers virtually the whole of the natural world, including the solar system, geology, plants, animals, adaptation to environment, instinct, behaviour and human anatomy and physiology.

It was written in English, in his own unique style, and provided a fascinating blend of scientific lore[2] coupled with his superb logic and great humility. Quite understandably, it was his most widely-read and popular work. Over the next one hundred and fifty years it ran to over twenty editions[3] and became his most influential book.

Gilbert White, a later clerical naturalist, was certainly one of those influenced. In his *Natural History of Selborne,* is a copy of a letter he wrote on August 1, 1771 to Daines Barrington, which contains the now-famous passage: *'But our countryman, the excellent Mr Ray, is the only describer that conveys some precise idea in every term or word, maintaining his superiority over his followers and imitators, in spite of the advantage of fresh discoveries and modern information.'*

William Paley, in his *Natural Theology* of 1802, incorporated most of Ray's *Wisdom*, without acknowledgement. This in turn became one of the most influential books of the early nineteenth century, and Darwin refers to it in his autobiography[4]. As Raven (1942, p.412) says of the *Wisdom*: *'more than any other single book it initiated the true adventure of modern science, and is the ancestor of the Origin of Species.'*

Much of the book is still of great interest today, both from the historical viewpoint, and for its natural history observations. A few samples of his writings are given below, to illustrate some of these.

In referring to *'How manifold are thy Works, O Lord'*, Ray comments that he will *'briefly run over the Works of the visible world and give some guess at the number of them.'* Stars are infinite, fossils he cannot guess, but on 'beasts' he gives what is probably the best-informed estimate of his times. Animals he puts at 150 species (including serpents), birds at near to 500, and his calculation for insects, based on his great local knowledge, is of particular interest: (pp.8-9) *'I find the number of such of these alone as breed in our neighbourhood [about Braintree and Notley in Essex] to exceed the summ I last year assigned to all England, having myself observed and described about 200 Kinds great and small, many yet remaining, as I have good reason to believe, by me undiscovered. If then within the small compass of a mile or two there are so many species to be found...Wherefore using the same argumentations, the number of all the British Insects will amount to 2,000, and the total sum of those of the whole Earth will be 20,000.'*

Taking next, the second line of the psalm, he says he will look at how the Works of God are *'all very wisely contrived and*

adapted to ends both particular and general.' e.g. details of
the geometry of the bees' honeycomb: (p.123) *'There are only
three rectilineous and ordinate figures which can serve to this
purpose..[Ordinate figures are such as have all their sides and
all their angles equal.] The three ordinate figures are
Triangles, Squares and Hexagons. For the space about any point
may be filled up either by six equilateral Triangles, or four
Squares, or three Hexagons. Of these the bee makes use of the
Hexagon, both because it is more capacious than either of the
other, provided they be of equal compass... and lastly, because
in the other figures more angles and sides must have met
together at the same point and so the work could not have been
so firm and strong.'*

Several pages are devoted to observations on the seeds of
plants. e.g.: (p.100) *'And it is remarkable that such Mosses as
grow upon walls, the roofs of houses and other high places, have
seeds so excessively small, that when shaken out of their
vessels they appear like vapour or smoak, so that they may
either ascend of themselves, or by an easie impulse of the wind
be raised up to the tops of houses, walls or rocks: and we need
not wonder how the Mosses got thither, or imagine they sprung up
spontaneously there.'*

In looking at *'the exact fitness of the parts of the bodies
of animals to their nature and manner of living'* he gives many
examples. e.g. the Woodpeckers: (p.132-3) *'They have a tongue
which they can shoot forth to a very great length, ending in a
sharp stiff bony tip, dented on each side; and at pleasure
thrust it deep into the holes, clefts and crannies of trees to
stab and draw out insects lurking there, and also into
anthills...Moreover, they have short, but very strong legs, and
their toes stand two forwards, two backwards, which disposition
Nature, or the Wisdom of the Creator, hath granted to
Woodpeckers, because it is very convenient for the climbing of
trees[5], to which also conduces the stiffness of the feathers of
their tails, and their bending downwards, whereby they are
fitted to serve as a prop for them to lean upon, and bear up
their bodies.'*

His reference to Aristotle's observations on the feet of
animals must have produced many smiles amongst his readers over
the years: (p.146) *'All animals have even feet, not more on one
side than the other; which if they had, would either hinder
their walking, or hang by not only useless, but also
burdensome...So we see, nature hath made choice of what is most
fit, proper, and useful. They have also not only an even number
of feet, answering by pairs one to another, which is as well
decent as convenient; but those too of an equal length, I mean
the several pairs; whereas were those on one side longer than
they on the other, it would have caused an inconvenient halting
or limping in their going.'*

NOTES TO CHAPTER 8

1. Psalm 104.24. Used by Ray as the heading on page 1.(NB. Page
   numbers given here, are from the second edition of 1692.)
2. It is still a treasure-trove of natural history lore today.
3. See Lisney, 1960, p.14.
4. e.g. 1892, p.18 (Freeman 1461).
5. Teleological arguments (i.e. developments are due to the
   purpose served by them.) such as this, are common throughout
   the book, and would not be generally accepted today.

CHAPTER 9

MISCELLANEOUS WORKS

OBSERVATIONS.

The *Observations* was published in 1673, seven years after his tour of the continent. It had the impressive title: *Observations, Topographical, Moral, & Physiological; Made in a Journey Through part of the Low-countries, Germany, Italy, and France, with A Catalogue of Plants not Native of England, found Spontaneously growing in those parts, and their Virtues. Whereunto is added A brief Account of Francis Willughby, Esq; his Voyage through a great part of Spain.'*

As far as Ray was concerned, the catalogue of plants (covered earlier on pages 31 and 43) was the main item. This is indicated in the preface, as after mentioning it, he continues: *'...considering the paucity of those who delight in studies and enquiries of this nature, to advantage the Catalogue I have added thereto a brief narrative of our whole voyage.'*

The 'brief' narrative fills 499 pages and covers an extraordinary range of topics, written in English. (The essay on fossils has already been covered in chapter 6). Full details are given of towns, trades, local governments, buildings, statues, geography, topography, geology, food, customs, taxation, modes of travel, and many other subjects including mechanical devices, and of course copious natural history observations.

It only contained four plates, and one of these, which was borrowed from another work, is shown overleaf. The following typical description (p.5) accompanies it: *'We saw the manner of raising up water for the use of citizens by a chain whereon are fastened cylindrical iron buckets. This chain is round in form of a bracelet, neck-lace or wheel-band, and put over a large axis deeply furrowed, from which it hangs down into a well of water, and being turned about by the axis, the descending buckets have their mouths downward, and take up water as they pass through the well; which they bring up to the axis, to which so[1] soon as they are come, by reason of their position they must needs turn it out into a trough placed under the axis, by which it is conveyed to a cistern, and thence by pipes to private houses. This kind of machin(e) is generally used in Italy, Spain and France, to water their gardens in summertime.'*

Though the biological observations are the best-documented and most readable, it contains a wealth of data of interest to students of history and many other disciplines, exemplifying yet again the multi-faceted mind of John Ray. A second edition was issued in 1738.

A COLLECTION OF CURIOUS TRAVELS AND VOYAGES.

In a letter[2] to Ray dated 25 October, 1692, Charles Hatton, to whom the *Historia Plantarum* had been dedicated, wrote concerning the *Itinerary* of Rauwolfius: *'...being printed about a hundred years since, it is very rare, and being never translated out of High Dutch, it is unintelligible to those who do not understand the German tongue.'* A translation was in preparation and *'should be corrected by a master of the English Language...for which achievement there is no person on earth so duly qualified as the justly-renowned Ray.'*

At first, Ray would not accept this editorial task, but later when he saw some of the work, he was sufficiently impressed to change his mind. Writing[3] to Sloane on April 10, 1693, he commented: *'I wonder indeed that so good a book hath lyen so*

An Engine to raise water with a chain of Bucket
taken out of Kircher's MVNDVS SVBTERRANE

pag.

Illustration from Ray's *Observations*
borrowed from Kircher's *Mundus Subterraneus*.

long locked up in High Dutch. I have revised it...A catalogue of more rare Oriental plants, I have drawn up, to be added at the end of the work.'
It was published in two volumes in 1693, and covered many countries including Syria, Palestine, Mesopotamia, Assyria, Greece, Asia minor, Egypt and Ethiopia. Later editions appeared in 1705 and 1738. (Keynes, 1951, pp.120-2).

PERSUASIVE TO A HOLY LIFE.
Along with the *Miscellaneous Discourses* and *Wisdom of God*, the *Persuasive* reflects Ray's religious thinking. For most of his life he had produced scientific writings, rather than those relating to his profession – divinity. His illness during the winter of 1699-1900, combined with one of his rare slack periods, probably prompted this attempt to redress the imbalance.
In the preface he gives the purpose as *'conducive to my preparation for that change which the pains and infirmity I laboured under seemed to threaten.'* (Raven, 1942, p.299). It was published in 1700 as a small book of only 133 pages, and contained little that was new or original. In style and content it was dull and uninspiring, and though later editions appeared in 1719 and 1745, it was probably his least popular work.

NOTES TO CHAPTER 9
1. In the texts of seventeenth century books in English, an 'f' was used in most places instead of an 's'. Thif if not eafy to read faft at firft but one foon getf ufed to it.
2. *Correspondence,* pp.255-6.
3. Idem, pp.262-3.

*　　*　　*　　*　　*　　*　　*　　*

JOHN RAY AND THE FUTURE.

In John Ray, Black Notley, Braintree, Essex, and indeed all of England, have a hero. As a man, he had in abundance, those qualities admired by his fellow creatures: humility, sincerity, intellectual honesty, readiness to give credit to others and an amazing capacity for hard work. As a scientist and natural historian, his range of comprehension, breadth of vision, and achievements, were greater than those of his contemporaries, and possibly of any of his successors. He brought order out of chaos, and laid the foundations, in more spheres of natural science, than probably any man who ever lived.
He instilled in British people, a love of natural history and the world about them – **this was his chief legacy to us.**
It is now our duty to protect that legacy, by conserving our countryside, so that future generations can, like Ray be:

'Fascinated and then absorbed by the rich spectacle of the meadows in spring-time (and)...filled with wonder-and delight by the marvellous shape, colour and structure of the individual plants.'

BIBLIOGRAPHY and REFERENCES.
ARBER, A. 1912 *Herbals Their Origin and Evolution.* 2nd ed. 1938.
ARBER, A. 1943. A seventeenth-century naturalist: John Ray. *Isis* **34**: 319-324.
BALDWIN, S.A. 1986. John Ray (1627 - 1705) Essex Naturalist. (In press). *Watch over Essex. Jl. Essex. Nat. Trust.*
BRIGGS, D. & WALTERS, S.M. 1969. *Plant variation and evolution.* 2nd. ed. 1984.
CROWTHER, J.G. 1960. *Founders of British Science,* 94-130.
CUVIER, G. and DUPETIT - THOUARS, A. 1824. *In Bibliographie Universelle,* **XXXVII**: 155-63, or 2nd ed, 1843, **XXXV**: 252-6.
DANDY, J.E. 1958. (ed.) *Sloane Herbarium,* 189-92.
DILLISTONE, F.W. 1975. *Charles Raven, Naturalist, Historian and Theologian. (The life of Ray's biographer).*
DEREHAM, W. (ed.) 1718. *Philosophical Letters, between the late learned Mr Ray and several of his ingenious Correspondents.*
DEREHAM, W. (ed.) 1760. *Select Remains of the learned John Ray.* Reprinted as *Memorials of John Ray* by the Ray Society in 1846, with additions.
DESMOND, R. 1977. *Dictionary of British and Irish Botanists and Horticulturists including Plant Collectors and Botanical Artists.* (Gives a useful bibliography up to 1975.)
DUNCAN, J. 1843. 'Memoir of Ray' *in The Natural History of Beetles:* Jardine's Naturalist's Library, **XXXV**: 17-70.
EWEN, A. H. and PRIME, C. T. (eds) n.d. [1975] *Ray's Flora of Cambridgeshire.* English translation.
GIBBON, E. 1695. *'Camden's Britannia,* London. (Ray produced the Catalogues of Plants for each County, except for Middlesex).
GIBSON, G.S. 1862. *Flora of Essex.*
GILMOUR, G.S.L. 1944. *British Botanists.*
GILMOUR, G.S.L. (ed.) 1972. *Thomas Johnson. Journeys in Kent and Hampstead.*
GILMOUR, G.S.L. & WALTERS, S.M. 1954. *Wild Flowers.*
GREEN, J.R. 1914. *A History of Botany in the United Kingdom from the earliest Times to the End of the 19th Century.*
GREGORY, W.K. 1910. The Orders of Mammals. *Bull. Amer. Mus. Nat. Hist.* **27.** New York.
GUNAWARDENA, D.C. 1933.*'Studies in the Biological Works of John Ray.'* Unpublished M.Sc. thesis, University of London.
GUNTHER, R.T. 1922. *Early British Botanists and their Gardens.*
GUNTHER, W.T. (ed.) 1928. *Further Correspondence of John Ray.*
GUNTHER, W.T. 1934. Letters from John Ray to Peter Courthope. *Journal of Botany.* **72**: 217-223.
GUNTHER, W.T. 1937. *Early Science in Cambridge.*
HALLER, Albrecht von. 1771. *Bibliotheca Botanica,* I, 500-6.
HARVEY-GIBSON. R.J. 1919. *Outlines of the History of Botany.*
HAWKS, E. 1928. *Pioneers of Plant Study.*
HENREY, B. 1975. *British Botanical and Horticultural Literature before 1800.* 3 vols.
HOENIGER, F.D. & J.F.M. 1969. *The Development of Natural History in Tudor England & The Growth of Natural History in Stuart England From Gerard to the Royal Society.*
KEYNES, G.L. 1951. *John Ray: a Bibliography.*
KEYNES, G.L. 1976. *John Ray, 1627 - 1705: a Bibliography, 1660-1970.*
KNIGHT, D.M. 1972. *Natural Science Books in English 1600-1900.*
LANKESTER, E. (ed.) 1846. *Memorials of John Ray.*
LANKESTER, E. (ed.) 1848. *The Correspondence of John Ray.* A reprint of *Philosophical Letters* with additional letters.

LINDLEY, J. 1826. In *Penny Cyclopaedia*, XIX, 317-19.
LISNEY, A.A. 1960. *A Bibliography of British Lepidoptera 1608-1799*. (It contains several Ray references not in Keynes).
MAYR, E. 1982. *The Growth of Biological Thought*.
MORTON, A.G. 1981. *History of Botanical Science*.
MIAL, L.C. 1912. *The Early Naturalists. Their Lives and Work*.
OLIVER, F.W. 1913. *Makers of British Botany*.
PATTISSON, J.H. 1847. John Ray. In *The Englishwoman's Magazine*, May 1847, II, 257-75.
PETIVER, J.A. 1719. *A Catalogue of Ray's English Herbal*.
PRIOR, R.C.A. 1879. *On the Popular Names of British Plants*.
PULTENEY, R. 1790. *Historical and Biographical Sketches of the Progress of Botany in England*.
RAVEN, C.E. 1941. New Light on John Ray. *Proc. Lin. Soc. London*. **154:** 3-10.
RAVEN, C.E. 1942. *John Ray Naturalist. His Life and Works*. [2nd. ed. 1950, reprinted April 1986 (in paper) with a new introduction by S.M.Walters.] **The definitive source.**
RAVEN, C.E. 1947. *English Naturalists from Neckham to Ray*.
SACHS, J. 1890. *History of Botany (1530-1860)*. Translated and revised by Garnsey, H.E.F and Balfour, I.B.
SEWARD, A.C. 1937. *John Ray*.
SMITH, J.E. 1819. The Life of John Ray, in *Rees' Cyclopaedia*. Reprinted in Lankester, E. 1846.
STANLEY, E. 1826. 'Philosophical Correspondence of Ray and Willughby', in *Restrospective Review*, XIV, 1-31.
STEARN, W.T. 1965. William Turner's 'Libellus', 1538, and 'Names of Herbes' 1548. Prefixed to Ray Society facsimile of Turner: *Libellus. The Names of Herbes*.
STEARN, W.T. 1973. Ray, Dillenius and the 'Synopsis methodica Stirpium Britannicarum'. Prefixed to Ray Society facsimile of Ray, *Synopsis methodica*. London (Ray Society).
STEARN, W.T. 1977. Historical Introduction in Desmond, R: *Dictionary of British and Irish Botanists & Horticulturists*.
STEARN, W.T. 1981. John Ray's 'Dictionariolum trilingue' a forgotten vocabulary. Prefixed to Ray Society facsimile of Ray, *Dictionariolum trilingue*.
STEARN, W.T. 1983. *Botanical Latin*. 3rd. ed.
SWANN, H.KIRKE. 1912. *A Dictionary of English and Folk Names of British Birds, with their History, Meaning and first Usage*.
TRIMEN, H. 1870. Notes of Ray's Hortus Siccus. *J. Bot.* **8:** 82-84.
WALTERS, S.M. 1981. *The Shaping of Cambridge Botany*.
WEBSTER, C. 1975. Ray, John. *In* C. Gillispie (Ed.), *Dictionary of Scientific Biography*, **11:** 313-318.
WELCH, M.A. 1972. Francis Willoughby, F.R.S. (1635-1672). *J.Soc. Biblphy nat.Hist.* **6:** 71-85.
WHEWELL, W. 1857. *History of the Inductive Sciences*, III.

OTHER SOURCES.

Of the many other sources too numerous to give in detail, mention should be made of the standard county floras such as: DRUCE, G.C. 1897. *Flora of Berkshire*, most of which have a section on Ray; the *Journal of Botany*, includes several other references in addition to those above, and various local publications have had a number of articles over the years, e.g: ***ESSEX COUNTRYSIDE***: 1952 (1), 1955 (4), 1959 (8), 1960 (9), 1970 (18) and 1986 (34); ***ESSEX NATURALIST***: 1890 (4), 1912/13 (17); ***ESSEX REVIEW***: 1916 (25), 1917 (26): *TRANS*. ***ESSEX FIELD CLUB***: 1886 (4).

INDEX

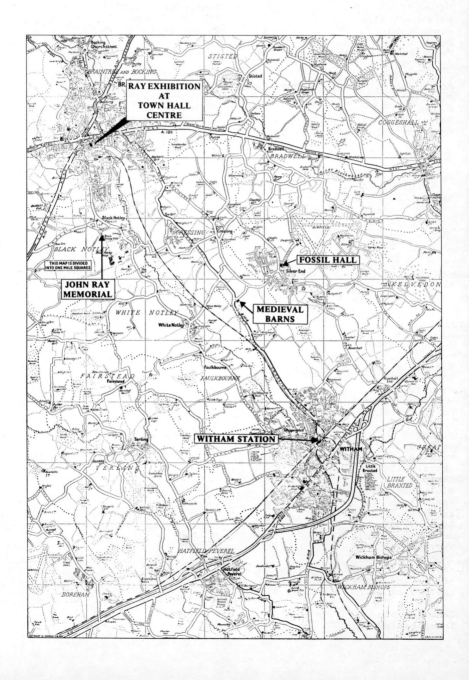